Homer Illustrated
Vol. I: Iliad

Written and illustrated By Irene Tahataki
Translated and rewritten by George J. Doundoulakis

Copyright (C) 2004, Irene Tahataki & George J. Doundoulakis

PRINTING:
TYPOKRETA • Tel.: 2810-380882 • Heraklion - Crete - Greece

Homer Illustrated

Vol. I: Iliad

CONTENTS

ILLUSTRATIONS

viii

Preface
By Irene Tahataki

It has been widely accepted that Homer's poems, the "Iliad" and the "Odyssey" are a true reflection of the Greek spirit as it blossomed about three millennia ago. Homer's poems have warmed not only the Greek soul, but that of everyone who became interested to envision the enchantment of exciting accounts in the life of the human beings of the time. Generations came and went but Homer's epics have been destined to stay young and beautiful for ever.

We do not know how these epics made it through the centuries; we probably owe it to the minds of Greek bards, who sang them as a final fulfillment during ceremonials and taught them to those of the next generation. But we are happy to have them as beacons of the human spirit and inspiration for new creations.

Many famous scholars have spent their lives reading and analyzing the epics; some taught their findings to us. Others, with their own talent and imagination, created their own epics, in their own dialect and style. Two such works have been"Erophile" by Hortatsis and "Erotokritos" by Kornaros, written about four centuries ago, in Cretan dialect, and fifteen-syllable rhyme verse.

I was a school teacher when I felt the urge to experiment with the fifteen-syllable rhyme verse using as subjects selected incidents from the "Iliad" and the "Odyssey". I immediately found that I was better able to impress and excite the imagination and emotions of my students by reading this verse to them, at the end of the class; When they started asking me for photo copies to bring to their parents, I made sure I had them ready for them. After a few years, I understood I possessed an inherent skill in writing verse which drove me to do more and more lines. Then, when I noticed that colored illustrations, along the subject discussed, also added to the ease of communicating with the student, I started with a few illustrations first, then kept painting illustrations as I wrote.

The number of lines grew from hundreds to thousands, at which time I had to make a decision, whether I was ready to commit myself to the colossal project of doing both Iliad and Odyssey in their entirety, or stop altogether. At the time,

I distributed the material that I already had completed into the established 24 rhapsodies and I found there were still big gaps left to fill; but I still decided to complete the work. After several years of hard work, 14000 lines and 100 illustrations for the two books, "Iliad" and "Odyssey", I was there; each book took around 7000 lines of verse and 50 color illustrations. I feel sure this work, will give the children's innate curiosity and thirst for learning additional impetus, beyond the simple coverage of Homer's understanding required by the school curriculum.

I was gratified to hear from friends of various ages who read both books that my work was equally interesting and enjoyable to all. One of those friends was Mr. George Doundoulakis, who later accepted to translate both books into English prose while adding material for emphasizing the points where Homer provides information as to the customs of his time.

Besides the material provided by Homer additional stories have been added to provide information to the background of the "Iliad", including stories about the Gods and Goddesses who are part of the plot. Actually, Homer's Iliad does not begin until the Chapter about "The Anger of Achilleus" and ends with the burning of the body of Hector. The information presented before this point has come from other sources and mainly mythology. Similarly the information about Achilleus' death, the Trojan Horse and the sucking of Troy, comes from different sources and serves well as an epilog to complete the story. Homer used "Iliad" as the background for the Odyssey and Odysseus as the link between the two.

I am happy to have made the decision to do this work and also happy to be able to offer it now with my sincere love to both our children and grownups.

Irene Tahataki
Archanes, Heraklion, Crete, Greece

Editor's note
By Manuel Vlieg

Editing this book was a pleasure; besides the beauty of the story, it gave me the opportunity to appreciate how much information Homer's epics provide. It was like opening a door to the past. With the door open a small bit I could see the plot of the Iliad and then the adventures of Odysseus on his way home. Opening the door wider and I saw the qualities of the privileged few, their heroes and their gods. It took a full open door to see how the underprivileged lived and thought. I wouldn't dare step through the door, unless I had reliable assurance, like from Zeus himself, I would be one of the privileged. With the door fully open, I looked at every detail, of the life at the time: how they visualized their gods, how their houses looked, what people wore, what they ate and what some of their customs were.

After closing the door I looked back at what I saw and liked and what I disliked and what was not quite answered, about which I still wonder. For example, I liked the way guests were treated in those days; when, upon arrival, the guests were washed and anointed with oil before they were brought to a table in the dining area; water was brought to wash their hands, then bread, then meats and wine. Nobody asked them who they were and what was the purpose of their visit until they finished eating. I also liked the fact that Zeus expected everyone to be cordial and helpful in general, and especially to strangers. This idea set the foundation that with time established a code of ethics, which could be useful even today and probably necessary in those times, where there appeared to be no established laws, besides what the person of a higher rank or the master dictated. Then, I found the interesting idea, what Zeus himself presented in the "Odyssey", "that people most of the time are themselves to blame for their troubles due to their own actions, rather than blaming the gods." Finally it was interesting to see that the women of the time, such as Helen, Hector's wife Andromache and Odysseus wife Penelope, were outspoken with substantial wisdom, undistinguishable from the women of today.

I was unhappy to see that outbursts of cruelty occurring in our world from time to time have not been a recent phenomenon, but was occasionally displayed since ancient times. Poseidon, turns the Phaeacian ship and its crew into stone, for helping Odysseus get back to Ithaca. Odysseus kills a hundred suitors and the maids that had dared form relationships with the suitors. Athena the goddess of wisdom not only condones but also orchestrates the killings; then later saves Odysseus from being punished. It is encouraging to see that as the social structure improves towards democracy and people's rights are being recognized, cruelty is generally contemned.

Still, there are a lot of mysteries and inadequate information. For example, we all know the Olympian gods resided on top of Mt. Olympus, that is why the adjective "Olympian". Why, then, as shown in the illustration on page (41), did the "Horas" had to open the "gates of Heaven" so that Athena's carriage for her and Hera, could go through. Could it be the gods actually resided in the portion of the sky over Mt. Olympus? Then let us consider the limitations of their gods, Poseidon is only able to see Odysseus' raft approaching Scheria after flying back north from Ethiopia, but not before. Similarly, Zeus goes and sits on top of Mt. Ida, near the battlefield, to better observe the battle. Aphrodite and Ares are wounded and feel pain. These power restrictions are simply an extension of the qualities of the Olympian gods who had been created in the image of the people; they are particularly striking to us because they are not in line with our present beliefs about gods.

Their diet, as mentioned in the epics, consisted of nothing but bread and meat from large animals: oxen, sheep, goats, pigs and the deer Odysseus killed by at Circe's island. With a large sea coast Greece should have had invented fishing. And the only fowls mentioned were the ducklings killed by an eagle in Penelope's dream and pigeons chased by eagles; nothing about chickens and small animals like rabbits. Again, nothing about fruit, although the presence of fruit trees has been acknowledged in several places.

Was it a coincidence that the tree growing over Charybdis, an evil place, was a fig tree, the kind of tree on which Satan, in the form of a snake, tempted Eve with an apple in the Garden of Eden? Was the olive tree, on which Odysseus supported his bridal bed, and therefore his marriage, the tree that provided the dove with a twig to tell Noah the deluge had ended and that he, his family and cargo could again inhabit the Earth?

Manuel H. Vlieg

Introduction
By George J. Doundoulakis

Homer's epics, *"Iliad"* and *"Odyssey"*, have delighted and moved the human heart for almost three millennia. Since the time of antiquity they molded the Greek spirit with grandeur, by embracing integrity and self esteem, ideas which grew and later moved west to form the basis of our contemporary humanism.

While there is some controversy as to whether the entire work should be credited to Homer, it is probably safe to assume that between the time of the Trojan war and Homer's time, some 300 to 500 years later, stories and poems of its heroes abound. These stories were narrated to grand children at the fireplace, and sang by bards and ordinary people. Homer, who according to some was a blind bard, possessed the talent of gathering what he needed and was found available, to interweave the marvel of the *"Iliad"*. With that done Homer could then jump into the *"Odyssey"*, starting with the myths and stories being circulated at the time. This sequence of events can explain why the *"Odyssey"* appears to cover much later time than the *"Iliad"*.

For more than two centuries Homer's epics were preserved in the minds of bards, who had an interest to learn, sing and teach others; some of them memorized both epics. About 550 B.C., Peisistratus, who claimed to be a descendant of Nestor, king of Pylos, was established as tyrant of Athens and gave orders for the assembly and writing of a text of the two epics, for the purpose of being recited during the "Panathenaea celebrations". It has been suggested that it was Peisistratus who provided his name for the son of Nestor in the *"Odyssey"*. Both epics were reviewed and adjusted approximately to their present form, four centuries later (150 B.C.), by Aristarchus of Samothrace, a well known ancient philologist.

For the inquisitive mind, reading Homer's poems is like conducting an archeological excavation. Both provide information about the lives of people that occupied same space on Earth centuries or millennia ago. The deeper an object is found in an excavation, the older the likelihood of its age. The age of creation of a particular story can sometime be guessed by details in its content. For example, Iron changed from being a precious metal at the time of the Trojan war, to becoming commonplace by Homer's time. We may suspect that the story where

Agamemnon sends ten <u>iron</u> cauldrons to Achilleus as a present for coming back to fight, was reflecting a time closer to Homer than to the Trojan war. Another criterion of determining the age of a story is by the way people were looking at their gods in the story. During the first millennium B.C., we find a radical change in how people regarded destiny and their gods. In Iliad we find a strict Zeus, threatening to break the carriage of his wife Hera and daughter Athena from underneath them if they continued disobeying him and helping the Greeks; he orders his brother Poseidon off the battlefield. In "Odyssey", a nicer Zeus grants Athena's request to order Calypso to free Odysseus and later to stop the relatives from revenging the slaying of the suitors by Odysseus. We also notice that while in Iliad it is suggested, not to even mention "Heaven's name in vain", in "Odyssey", bard Demodocus, sings a song of a scandal about Hephaestus discovering an affair between Aphrodite and Ares. As for "The will of the gods and the firmness of destiny" we note that while in Iliad not even Zeus could have changed the destiny of his son Sarpedon when his Fate showed he was doomed to die, Odysseus, a mortal in "Odyssey", is able to save himself from the rage of Poseidon a number of times using his wits and courage. With time, people came to understand that it was their own actions rather than the will of the gods that shaped their destiny.

Homer put his poems together to both entertain and teach. He entertains by testing the human being struggling under extraordinary circumstances, generating wonder and exciting every human emotion. He teaches by having his characters act properly, according to his own code of ethics, or badly. Then, by rewarding the proper behavior and punishing the unruly, Homer establishes a code of ethics and justice, using the gods to do the punishing or provide the reword. He dealt with the rich and powerful because it was the high class that had molded the society before and at his time, while the poor people had relatively little to say, they were unimportant. When Agamemnon asked his soldiers whether they would accept to abandon their effort to occupy Troy and go back home after having lost so many comrades and having gone through so much suffering for nine years, they all answered "Yes", they wanted to go home and did not care about capturing Troy. They knew the glory and the treasures of Troy would have benefitted only the chiefs and not themselves.

Yet, from Homer we also find out about the ordinary people as they interact with the powerful. For example, we learn how Briseis, Achilleus slave woman, felt when Patroclus died, in Iliad; and we learn, in "Odyssey" about the life of Eumeus, a slave placed in charge of the pigs. We also learn about the maid Euryclea, who although a slave, had been placed in charge of the other maids and was the only one to keep the key to the storage room, sort of being second in command under Penelope; yet she was assigned to wash the feet of Odysseus, a guest. As the Olympian gods and goddesses were created in the image of ordinary people, we indirectly learn about their thoughts, sentiments, scandals and arguments by studying how their gods and goddesses felt and behaved. Particular effort has been made in this book to cover such information in relative detail, without taking away from the story. It is important to find out whether people as back as three thousand years ago, thought and behaved like us, better or worse, under similar circumstances. Such a comparison may give us clues as to the evolution or rigidity of the human personality.

Besides Homer's description of how people thought and acted in his time, he also provides abundant information about what they wished they could be, in terms of what they considered to be their Heroes; although he warns nothing comes free. Achilleus the hero in the Iliad is a nobleman, a glory seeking fighter, forever victorious, almost immortal. But in grief, after his friend Patroclus death, he loses control of himself, he becomes vindictive to the point of savagery against the Trojans, kills Hector, his adversary, and dishonors his body; while he himself falls into deep despair. His humane nature returns only when Hector's father, Priam, reminds him of his father when he comes to his tent and begs for the body of his son. Not only does he treat Priam with compassion, but he also washes and delivers Hector's body to him. Soon after, Achilleus was killed by Apollo, whom he dared antagonize.

However, Homer's favored Hero was Odysseus. During the Trojan war he is shown to be a smart talker, shrewd and inventive, always there to help during every emergency. His best contribution was the idea of the Trojan horse as the means for attacking Troy from within its city. In *"Odyssey"*, where his adventures on his way home are narrated, Homer is given the opportunity to describe Odysseus' complicated nature, the qualities one needed to survive during very difficult times. Without provocation he attacks and destroys Ismarus, a peaceful city, killing most of the men and taking the women and loot, which he divides amongst the men. Ten years later, he describes this adventure to the Phaeacians with no noticeable remorse; yet he cries when the bard Demodocus sings about an argument he had with Achilleus. When he meets people during his travels he lies about himself, a quality Athena interprets as a clever trick. He considers himself to be king of Ithaca, yet he first kills some one hundred young men who frequented his house as suitors of his wife, then Melanthius, a defector, and those maids who had dared establish relationships with the suitors, for having dishonored his house. Homer here shows plainly that the life of the slave women, who ended up to become maids in rich houses had no rights to establish relationships of their own, and they simply belonged to the master. While going through adventures during his travels Odysseus would do anything to survive.

On the good side, Odysseus was a brave fighter both in war and against the superhuman elements he met during his travels. He overcame unimaginable perils by using his self confidence, his strength and endurance to prevail at the end. But Odysseus character, as that of a hero, is used to mainly portray difficult times, where to survive one had to be hard, shrewd, lie and be selfish. That does not mean there were a lot of people like Odysseus around, it simply says it was difficult to succeed unless the individual was really tough.

In 1998 while in Crete with my wife, we visited a friend, Irene Taliatakis, in a small village called Archanais. Irene is a retired public school teacher, very modest and unassuming, until you get to know her. When we walked into her living room, we were astonished with the number of paintings spread all over. She explained she had just published two books "_Moments in Iliad_" and "_Moments in Odyssey_", each close to three hundred pages, chosen sections of Homers' epics in the form of poems in the Cretan dialect. She explained that as she was writing, she was also painting, about one hundred scenes of Homeric events, most of which she included in her books. I was highly impressed, as she was neither a known painter nor poet, but I could see she was extremely talented. Once I started reading her poems, I found them so beautiful, I couldn't stop; after I finished reading both books, I happened to meet with Irene again. I expressed my admiration for her work and suggested a book in prose, where, along with the simple story, all information about the customs of the time and the people's mentality of their gods and their heroes, as they appear in Homer, could be emphasized and presented in relative detail. "How about doing that in English", she replied, "I will provide the information you will need in Greek for you to translate into English, while you add the information you want to emphasize. In addition, you can use my illustrations as you please." I said, I will think about it, but I knew I was hooked and soon I agreed. Since my school days I was fascinated with Homer. During my retirement I often visit the particular shelf in the library where I always can find books pertaining to Homer's epics. Now, I would have the opportunity to devote more time to the subject in doing something I could enjoy. Indeed, by using the information which Irene sent me, including substantial information from mythology to use as a background, for the story, I established the foundation to which I could easily add the details I thought should be emphasized. With three years of intensive research, selecting, writing and rewriting, Homer illustrated, in terms of two volumes, *"Iliad"* and *"Odyssey"* came to its final shape. I am indebted to my friend, Manuel Vlieg, and to my daughter-in-law, Lori April Douglas, for the editing, and to Arthur Ingoglia for the final checking of the books.

G. J. D

HOMERIC MAP

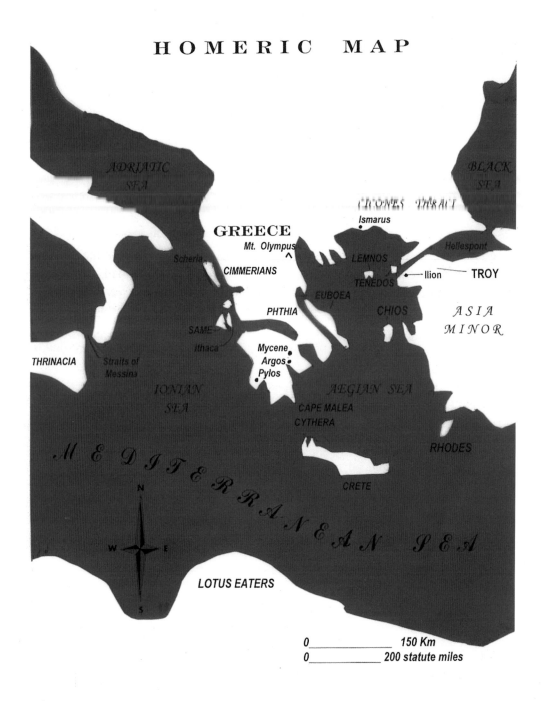

PART ONE:
Background

I. PARIS OF TROY IS BORN

About 1200 BC, there was in the northwest corner of Asia Minor a rich country called Troy, with a beautiful city known as Ilion. To the west of Troy, across the Aegean Sea there was the Greek Mainland, home of the Achaean. Under the rule of King Priam, Troy was rich and strong and its people were happy. One night, while Troy's Queen Hecuba was pregnant with her second child, she had a terrifying dream. She dreamed that she gave birth to a flaming torch, which went from house to house burning everything in its path until the city was reduced to ashes. Terrified, the Queen woke up and told the King about her dream. The King sent for his wisest seer, who interpreted the dream to mean that his unborn son would someday be responsible for the destruction of his beloved Troy. So, as soon as the baby was born, King Priam gave him to the shepherd Agelaio with instructions to take the baby to the mountain and kill him. Agelaio took the baby to the peak of Mount Ida, the highest mountain in the land, but did not have the heart to kill him. Instead, he placed the baby inside a hollow tree, and left him there.

But Agelaio could not get the baby out of his mind. He felt guilty for disobeying the instructions of his King, and was remorseful for having left the baby on the mountain alone, where he might starve to death or be eaten by wolves. A few days later, Agelaio returned to the mountain, where he was surprised to find a female bear cuddling the baby and nursing him like a good mother. He interpreted what he saw as being the will of the gods that the boy be saved, and soon thereafter he took the boy, whom he named "Paris" and raised him as his own.

II. THE TWELVE OLYMPIAN GODS, GODDESSES
AND LESSER GODS

Who were these gods who had willed that Paris should live? Back, in the days of Troy, people believed in many gods; the primary gods, known as the Olympian gods and numerous lesser gods.

The Olympian gods lived on top of Mount Olympus, the tallest mountain in Greece, which stood ten thousand feet above sea level. These gods had many of the qualities and weaknesses of ordinary people, except they were immortal. Zeus, (known by the Romans as Jupiter) was the king of all of the gods on Mount Olympus and was married to Hera (Juno). Zeus was regarded to be the ruler of the skies, where he controlled the clouds and punished whoever made him angry with a strike from his loud thunderbolts. He was the son of Rhea and Cronus (Saturn) whom he dethroned and banished from Olympus. It was not unusual for a father to be dethroned by his own son, as Cronus, son of Gaia (Terra), meaning Earth, had himself overthrown his father, Uranus (Coelus).

The twelve Olympian gods

Hestia (Vesta), the goddess of fire, Demeter (Ceres), and Poseidon (Neptune) were Zeus= older siblings. Folklore has it that their father Cronus swallowed all three of them at birth for fear that if they were allowed to grow up, they would endanger his throne. So, in order to save her next child, Zeus, Rhea secretly met with Cronus' father, Uranus, who advised her to go to the island of Crete to give birth on Mount Ida. After she gave birth, she left the baby Zeus to be nursed and raised with her cousins, the Nymphs, who were lesser goddesses. As a precaution, on the way back to Olympus, Rhea made a stone in the shape of a baby which she pretended to nurse. When Cronus saw the stone baby, he grabbed it, and like the previous children, swallowed it whole, unaware that he had eaten a stone instead of his new son. When Zeus was grown, he fought many battles on Mount Olympus until he finally defeated his father, Cronus. He forced Cronus to drink a magic potion, which made him nauseous, making him to throw up the other children, who were adults by then, as well as the stone. Since Cronus' children were gods, they were immortal and had survived all those years in their father=s belly. Needless to say, they were grateful to their brother, Zeus, for having liberated them, and they hailed him as the ruler of the universe and vowed their undying support and loyalty. Thus, in Zeus' palace, atop Mt.

Zeus seating on his throne with Hermes, Athena and the eagle.

Olympus, everything was ideal; the sun was always shining, and it never snowed. The gods ate delicious Ambrosia and drank delightful Nectar.

Zeus' brother, Poseidon, was the ruler of the seas. When angry, he would use his trident to churn the oceans and make the Earth tremble. Zeus' younger brother, Pluto (Dis), also known as Hades, was the ruler of the underworld and the souls of the dead. Since no woman would have voluntarily agreed to spend eternity in the underworld as Pluto's wife, Pluto kidnaped Persephone, the daughter of Demeter, from her home on Earth to become his Queen. Demeter, who was the goddess of agriculture, end-lessly traveled the Earth in search of her daughter.

It is said that Zeus had fifteen children. In our story, we will frequently encounter Pallas Athena (Minerva), who, they say, popped out of Zeus' forehead, fully grown and fully dressed, wearing a helmet on her head and holding a javelin in her right hand. She was to become the goddess of wisdom; as well as art and science, yet she was aggressive enough to fight with Ares (Mars), the god of war. Aphrodite (Venus), the goddess of love and beauty, was thought to have sprung up from the foam of the sea, but rumor has it she was really the daughter of Zeus and his mistress, Dione. According to the gossip of the time, Aphrodite had a love affair with Ares, the god of war. Another of Zeus' children, the ugly Hephaestus (Vulcan), husband of the beau-tiful Aphrodite, was the blacksmith of the gods. He worked underground, beneath the island of Lemnos, where he made ornaments for the gods using fire, metals and gems. Fire and smoke escaped through the surface of the Earth from time to time on the island of Lemnos from Hephaestus' blacksmith shop to form a volcano. Apollo, son of Zeus and Leto, also known as "Phoebus," was an artistic god, who had many tal-ents including the ability to play the harp. He carried a beautiful bow and quiver on his shoulder and did not hesitate to demonstrate his sharp shooting skills whenever he felt the urge. With the exception of Zeus and his mother Leto, the rest of the gods were all afraid of Apollo.

Hermes (Mercury) son of Zeus with Maia (daughter of Atlas) was the messenger and guide to the Gods.

Then, there were the lesser gods and goddesses. These lesser gods could take many non-human forms, such as a river or the dawn, which was thought to be a beautiful goddess who pulled away the veils of the night, allowing the light of the new day to shine through. We will learn about more gods and goddesses later.

Beautiful Dawn gloriously appears from behind the veils of the night.

III. HOMER

Homer is known as the author of the two famous epics, the *Iliad*, and the *Odyssey*. Homer has been described as a blind minstrel, who lived on one of the Greek islands, possibly Chios or Lemnos, some three to five hundred years after the end of the Trojan War. By then, the heroes of the war had become legends and stories and poems about them abounded. Homer took several of these stories and transformed them into magnificent poems, which he performed for food and shelter. Using his marvelous imagination, he filled in the gaps in these existing stories to compose his two epics, which still fascinate the readers, thousands of years later. *Iliad* tells the tale of a great war between the Trojans, the people from within and around the city of Ilion, of a region known as Troy, and the Achaians, the people of Greece. The war lasted for ten years and ended with the destruction of Troy. The story portrays the actions of heroes, gods and goddesses during the turning points in the struggle between the Trojans and the Achaians. *Odyssey*, which is presented as a sequel to *Iliad*, describes the adventures of Odysseus, one of the great heros of the Trojan war, as he struggles to return home after the destruction of Troy.

It takes grand deeds by legendary heroes to create an epic. What does it take to be a hero? Practically anyone who did something noticeable or admirable is considered a hero. Homer found an abundance of heroes in the warriors of the Trojan war

Homer, getting his inspiration from the Muse.

and their gods. The two main heroes of Homer's epics are Achilleus, in the *Iliad* and Odysseus, in the *Odyssey*. And there were also many celebrated women, the three goddesses, Hera, Athena and Aphrodite; Helen, the wife of Menelaos, and Andromache, the wife of Hector in *Iliad*, and Penelope and Athena in *Odyssey*. Each of Homer's epics takes more than three hundred pages, and each is considered a literary treasure. Imagine how much time and effort goes into excavating an archeological site, where every tiny article found is carefully examined in an attempt to understand how the ancient people lived and thought. Homer's epics provide an abundance of detailed information to educate us about the lives and gods of the ancient Greeks while entertaining us at the same time. In the following pages, we will not only be captivated by an illustrated story, we will have the opportunity to become archaeologists, sociologists and anthropologists, allowing ourselves to examine and analyze the wealth of information Homer passed on to us through his epic poems. While the gods who are so vividly depicted in his poems never existed in a physical sense, they certainly existed in the minds of the ancient Greeks where they were created. Thus, by studying the behavior of their gods and goddesses we learn how the ancient Greeks, men and women, thought and behaved.

Hera looks down as Helios drives the sun carriage across the sky.

Homer illustrates, by way of examples, the qualities, sentiments and weaknesses with which people of his time had endowed their heroes and their gods. He teaches us what conduct was considered proper and just and what was viewed as brutal behavior. We will learn how ancient people, in their quest for knowledge and because of their inherent curiosity to explain the causes of natural phenomena, created an array of Gods, each suited to fill a void and/or to explain a natural wonder. For example, thunder and lightning was caused by Zeus hurling his thunderbolts in anger. The daily phenomenon of the sun rising in the east and setting in the west was thought to occur by the god Helios, transporting the sun on a carriage across the sky, under the guidance of Apollo. After all, what other explanation could there be?

Homer himself did not fully understand how he came to have such a vivid imagination, so he explained it in terms of inspiration from the "Muses." There were nine Muses, all sisters, the daughters of "Mnemosyne," meaning memory. Each of the Muses represented a particular type of art. Since Homer was a poet, he believed that "Euterpe" and "Erato" were the Muses who inspired him. People were fascinated with Homer, who was not only a poet, but also an accomplished singer — even the gods used to gather around to listen when he sang.

Even the gods gathered around when Homer sang.

IV. THETIS WEDDING AND ERIS' APPLE

The nine sister Muses were outnumbered by the fifty Nereids, daughters of Nereus, all of whom were, therefore, sisters. The Nereids were beautiful maidens, and could sometimes be seen riding dolphins in the Mediterranean Sea or dancing on the beach. One of the Nereids, Thetis, was the mother of Achilleas, the hero of the Achaians in the Iliad. One day, Zeus admired her beauty, but she offended him by running away. To punish her, Zeus decreed that she marries Peleus, a mortal, and set the wedding date for the very next day.

Weddings were happy events for the gods, just as for mortals, and all of the gods, except Eris, were invited to partake in the celebration. Eris had been exiled from Mount Olympus for creating disharmony among the Gods. For revenge, at the wedding of Thetis and Peleus, she quickly flew by and dropped a golden apple on the wedding table with the words *"To the fairest"* inscribed on it. Hera, the first lady of Olympus, wise Athena and beautiful Aphrodite all immediately rose to claim the golden apple. Now, who in his right mind would dare to chose among these three beautiful goddesses? Even Zeus knew that would be dangerous territory. So, finally, Zeus ruled that a mortal would decide who was to get the prized apple. The mortal he chose was Paris, son of Priam, who by this time had grown into a handsome young

Gods and goddesses, all were invited to Thetis' wedding, except Eris.

man. Paris spent his time tending his father's sheep on Mount Ida, where he loved to sit under the trees playing the flute and singing. Hermes, the messenger of gods, guided the three Goddesses to where Paris sat.

At first, Paris was startled to see four godly shadows materializing in holy beauty before him, but Hermes reassured him that no harm would come to him. "Don't be afraid Paris these three goddesses need your help. Give this golden apple to the most beautiful of them," Hermes said and disappeared, going back to Olympus. The first goddess, Hera, approached Paris and said, "Paris, I am the first lady in the palace of gods, wife of Zeus, the cloud gatherer. Choose me and I will give you a kingdom greater than all of Asia." Then, the second goddess, Athena, spoke. "Paris, choose me and I will make you the wisest man in the world." Then, beautiful Aphrodite raised the fine veil, uncovering her head and shoulders, and said AParis, choose me and I will give you a wife almost as beautiful as me@. Paris was overwhelmed with Aphrodite's beauty and without hesitation, he gave her the golden apple. With that, the goddesses disappeared. Everything seemed normal on Mount Ida, but it was not: two powerful goddesses were disappointed and angry, and someone would have to pay the price.

After listening to what each had to offer, Paris gave the apple to Aphrodite.

V. HELEN

During this time, there was a woman named Helen, who was the daughter of King Tyndareus of Sparta, and his wife, Leda. Helen was believed to be the most beautiful woman in the world. Although Tyndareus thought Helen was his own daughter, in reality, her father was Zeus. One day, years before, Zeus was preparing for the Trojan war, and he needed a beautiful woman for his plan. As luck would have it, he came across the beautiful Leda, who was sunbathing. Zeus turned himself into an eagle and soared over to where Leda lay. He spread his wings over her body and flew away. Although she was startled with the eagle's behavior, she did not give it a second thought. Soon after, Leda realized she was pregnant. When the time came to have her baby, instead of giving birth to a child, Leda delivered two eggs. Startled, she hid the eggs and waited to see what would happen. A few days later, the eggs hatched before her eyes. Lo and behold, a cute baby girl emerged from one of the eggs. From the other egg, twin boys. Leda told her husband, Tyndareus, about the birth of his three beautiful children, but never of the eggs. They named the girl Helen, and the boys were named Kastor and Polydeukes, who grew up to become the Dioskouroi, protectors of the seamen.

The boys were protectors of their sister, Helen, as well as. When Helen was young, she was abducted by Theseus, an Athenian prince and was saved by her brothers, the Dioskouroi.

When Helen was old enough for marriage, suitors from all over Greece traveled to Sparta to ask her father for her hand. But Tyndareus was worried that by choosing one of the suitors to be his future son-in-law, he would make enemies of the other powerful princes. Odysseus, who had traveled to Sparta to ask Tyndareus for the hand of his niece, Penelope, had a solution to Tyndareus' dilemma. Odysseus suggested to Tyndareus that he let Helen choose her own mate, but only on the condition that all of the suitors take an oath promising that if Helen was ever abducted again, they would all help to rescue her and punish the assailant. All of the suitors were very anxious to be chosen by Helen so they readily accepted the terms and took the oath. Helen chose Menelaos as her husband, who was the son of Atreus, and had blond hair and blue eyes. He was rich and was the brother of Agamemnon, the powerful king of Mykenai.

Of course, Helen at this point had no idea of the deal Aphrodite had made with Paris, and was unaware that as the world's most beautiful woman, she had been promised to Paris in exchange for the golden apple.

VI. PARIS FINDS HELEN

The encounter with the goddesses had changed Paris. He suddenly felt as if the world was his for the taking. At this time, King Priam proclaimed that there would be Games to honor the death of a relative, and he sent his men to Mount Ida to select the best bull as a prize for the winner. But the bull they selected was Paris' pet which he had raised since birth. Paris realized that the only way he would be able to take the bull back would be to go to Troy to compete with the best of the Trojans in the games. And so he went, and with the help of the Goddess Aphrodite, Paris was able to defeat Priam's older son, Hector, the greatest fighter in all of Troy. The Trojans were greatly offended that a mere shepherd had beaten their best warrior, and Priam's son Deiphobos, accosted Paris, who fled to the temple of Zeus to escape. Once there, Priam's clairvoyant daughter, Cassandra, immediately recognized who he was and shouted, AThis is not a stranger, this is the son of Priam and Hecuba, who was secretly raised by Agelaio on Mount Ida." When the family heard the news, Paris' brothers and sisters (and they were forty-nine of them!) all came and embraced him with tears in their eyes.

His parents, Priam and Hecuba, were so proud of their son, they forgot the terror of the oracle and Hecuba's dream and welcomed him to the palace with the other children.

Paris easily adapted to life as a prince. Soon he met and married Oinone, the daughter of a nymph. But as lovely as Oinone was, Paris knew she was not the great beauty that Aphrodite had promised him.

One day, Paris decided to go on a journey to the land of Achaians, where he had heard there were many beautiful women. As an excuse, he pretended he was going to search for his aunt Isione, King Priam's sister, who had been abducted during a raid of Troy by Hercules and was later turned over to his son, Telamon. There were rumors that Telamon had sold Isione to the Dioskouroi in Sparta, but there was no information about Isione after their death. Priam, who had never forgotten his sister, gladly agreed to Paris' trip. He immediately ordered his men to find the tallest trees on Mount Ida to build a large ship for Paris. Paris was delighted, for now he would have his own ship, where he could entertain the beautiful woman Aphrodite had promised him. Priam arranged for several other ships to accompany Paris on the trip. When everything was ready and the winds blew from the north, the entire entourage raised sails; the ships leaped into the waves and from the top of the walls of Troy they looked like a flock of albatross.

As Paris' ships approached Sparta, they encountered another group of ships traveling south away from the mainland. These ships were the flotilla carrying Helen's husband, Menelaos to visit his friend Nestor, King of Pylos. The Trojans and Achaians admired each other's ships from afar.

When Paris finally reached Sparta, his first stop was the temple of Aphrodite, and the news soon spread among the people that a handsome prince from Troy was visiting their city. Helen, who had been left in charge of the palace during Menelaos' absence, immediately went to the temple to welcome the stranger and offer her hospitality. When Paris first saw beautiful Helen, he mistook her for Aphrodite, and when she introduced herself as Helen, his head spun; he knew immediately that this beauty was the woman Aphrodite had promised him. As Helen gazed at Paris' handsome face and delicate manners, she felt uncontrollably attracted to him, which puzzled and disturbed her, for she already knew she had fallen in love with him.

VII. PARIS AND HELEN FLEE FROM SPARTA

At the palace, Paris' party was treated with exceptional hospitality and when Paris asked Helen to meet him in the garden that evening, she nodded her agreement.

When she arrived at the garden later that night, Helen found a path of rose petals leading to a throne made of flowers. Paris took her by the hand and guided her to the throne. AYour beauty belongs among the flowers@, he said. She was speechless; no-one had ever talked to her that way, especially not Menelaos, who used to refer to her as his Afavored mare." Paris continued, AMy Goddess and my Queen, it is divine will that brought us together. The Goddess Aphrodite promised to give me the most beautiful woman on earth, and I know it is you. It is the will of the gods that you come live with me for eternity. Given the choice of a life in Sparta married to a barbaric man or a life of bliss with her beloved Paris, she quickly agreed. That same night, they gathered up their belongings and a few precious items from the palace and boarded the ship headed for Troy.

VIII. MENELAOS GOES TO TROY TO GET HELEN BACK PEACEFULLY BUT FAILS

When Menelaos returned to Sparta and learned that a Prince from Troy had snatched his wife and stolen his treasures, he was insulted, grief-stricken and angry. He enlisted a delegation of two other kings, Odysseus and Palamedes, to accompany him to Troy, where they demanded the immediate return of Helen. If Helen was not returned, they vowed to go to war and destroy Troy. When confronted by the three kings, Priam claimed to know nothing of Helen and told them that Paris had not yet returned. Priam had not forgotten, however, that it was a Greek, Hercules, that had abducted his sister Isione many years before. Priam's sons were greatly offended by the threats of the envoys and were eager to attack them. But Priam restrained them and assured the three kings that Aif Paris returns with the Greek woman, we will gladly return her to the Greeks, provided that they return my sister, Isione, at the same time." As their mission was unsuccessful, the envoys returned to Greece, where Menelaos immediately sent emissaries to his brother, Agamemnon and other prominent kings enlisting their help in declaring war on the Trojans and getting Helen back.

IX. WAR AGAINST TROY IS DECIDED

Most of the kings summoned by Menelaos volunteered to go to war against Troy. Others followed reluctantly, persuaded by Menelaos' brother Agamemnon, the powerful and influential king. But their main incentive was the quest for adventure, glory, and riches, as Troy was known to be a wealthy city.

1. Iphigenia in Aulis.

It took two years to ready the men and equipment for the campaign against Troy. A few groups of soldiers, who were anxious for adventure, left on their own, only to get lost, loot inconsequential lands and return. Eventually, Agamemnon managed to gather the troops together in Aulis where they prepared to set sail.

But the westerly winds needed to carry the sails across the Aegean, did not materialize, and Seer Calchas was summoned to offer help. Calchas concluded that the Goddess Artemis (Diana) was angry at Agamemnon because he had killed her deer, and in exchange, she demanded the sacrifice of Agamemnon's daughter, Iphigenia. At first, Agamemnon resisted the idea of sacrificing his own daughter, but in the end, he gave in. Although Iphigenia was brought to Aulis under the false pretense of her marriage to Achilleus, she ultimately consented to being sacrificed for the good of her people. Before she were to follow the heralds, she sent a dispatch to her mother Clytemnestra; "Mother", she said, AI was born not just for myself, but also for my country. Look at all these men, ready to sacrifice themselves in battle with the barbarians for the sake of their country. Dying for one's country is not death@. Then, she went with the heralds and they placed the sacred wreaths of sacrifice on her head, before they walked her to the Temple of Artemis, amidst the tears of the crowd. Legend says that Artemis replaced Iphigenia with an antelope at the last moment. But when a messenger arrived to inform Iphigenia's mother of the miracle she responded with, "Alas, I will never see my daughter again".

With the account of Artemis settled by the sacrifice of Agamemnon's daughter, the western winds materialized and carried the Achaean fleet across the Aegean Sea to Troy.

2. Cassandra is Concerned, but Troy Accepts Helen.

It is said that when Priam's daughter, Cassandra, caught a glimpse of Paris and Helen leaving the boat for the city of Ilion, she immediately became hysterical as she foresaw the consequences. She shouted, APeople of Troy beware, for it is a mortal sin to steal someone else's wife. I predict that the Achaians' armies shall come to punish and annihilate Troy". Naturally, the people of Troy were greatly alarmed and began to protest. Priam called for a meeting of the high council, which consisted primarily of his family members and the wealthiest of the citizens. Taking into consideration Helen's beauty and the vast treasures she brought to Troy, with the promise to share the wealth with the people, the high council decided to grant asylum to Helen, despite the continuing protests of the masses outside the palace. Priam and Hecuba summoned Helen to discuss her feelings and her plans for the future. Helen informed them that now that she has gotten to know Paris, she has fallen deeply in love with him and considers him her husband. She fell to her knees before Hecuba and pleaded with her to accept her as part of the family, rather than banishing her to Sparta, where she would endure great embarrassment. They agreed to treat her as if she were a stranger pleading for asylum, which they agreed to grant.

3.The Achaians are Here.

More than a year passed and life returned to normalcy in Troy. Then, one spring morning, the Trojans' worst fears were realized. Hundreds of ships suddenly appeared on the horizon. The ships soon arrived at the coast, at the mouth of the Scamander River, at the beginning of the Hellespont. As each boat reached the coast, the Achaean soldiers jumped out to secure to the land. Then, according to plan, some were assigned the job of digging a wide trench for protection from possible attack, while the rest began to prepare shelters for themselves, stables for their animals and warehouses to store their equipment and supplies. To the southeast, a couple of miles away, rose the formidable walls of the city of Ilion, with towers spaced all around.

4. The First Taste of Battle.

Before the Achaians had a chance to build their shelters, Hector, King Priam's son and Army General for the Trojan forces, had readied his horses, assembled his fighters, and ordered the city gates opened. The defenders of Troy were quickly out of the city walls and into the open plain. When the Achaians saw a cloud of dust rising in the direction of the walls of Troy, they knew they would soon be under attack. There was a lot of confusion amongst the Achaians, who retreated to their ships seeking their arms. By the time Hector's cavalry arrived, most of the Achaians had run back into the ships. Hector expected a quick victory; but, Achilleus quickly assembled his Myrmidons and counter-attacked. Now the Trojans were surprised and they hastily retreated to the safety of the walls of Troy. Several Trojans were killed by Achilleus and his men. The Achaians had one casualty, Protesilaos, who did not run to his ship but stood and fought the Trojans. He came up against Aeneas, leader of the Dardanians, one of the best Trojan fighters. He was believed to be the son of the Goddess Aphrodite and Anchises. Aeneas killed Protesilaos with a single arrow. Agamemnon ordered guards on a 24 hour watch. Then, he ordered the gathering of wood for the burning of the body of the first casualty with all honors due a real hero, and the building of a great monument at the tip of the peninsula where the ashes of Protesilaos would be buried.

E. A New Outlook of the War.

The Trojan attack was a rude awakening to the Achaians. If it weren't for brave Achilleus and his Myrmidons, the war would have ended within hours. Immediately after the burial of Protesilaos' ashes, Agamemnon called a meeting of all the rulers. They decided to build their own wall to protect their camp and especially their boats from sneak attacks by the Trojans. Until the wall would be finished, Achilleus with his Myrmidons would be kept on alert, ready to face any Trojan assault. In the mean time, the Trojans did not want to risk another encounter with Achilleus; instead they decided to stay within the safe walls of Troy. They knew they were in a better place to wait it out than the Achaians, who only had a limited amount of supplies, brought on the ships from Greece. Soon, the Achaians would have to venture away from the protection of the wall they built to look for food.

Besides the people inside the walls of Troy, the people of the entire valley were allies, friends and sympathizers of Troy. Every time the Achaians would venture out into the valley of Troy, they would be up against hostile populations. But, the Achaians had the advantage of surprise, they were better trained and ready for war. Despite fierce resistance, the outcome of sudden raids usually ended in favor of the Achaians. Eventually, after years of struggle, the people of the valley understood they had no recourse but to let the Achaians take whatever they wanted — water, grain, animals, and even their women.

F. No Early Solution to the War.

The years were passing with the Trojans and Achaians each protecting their own, with no resolution to the war in sight. From Homer's account, this was a war of the aristocracy, the leaders of the expedition. From the way the two rival armies fought we can conclude that the art of war was still in its infancy. It is also possible that Homer not being a military man, could not provide actual details. According to Homer, the primary goal of each of the leaders was to establish glory for himself. With the passage of time each side sized up the dangerous fighters of the other side, and each leader was looking to engage the one over whom he thought could prevail. Achilleus, despite his already established reputation of being the bravest and most dangerous of the Achaians, would not miss a single opportunity to add to his glory. The Achaians knew that Achilleus mother, the Nereid Thetis, soon after she had given birth, had dipped his body in the water of the fountain of immortality. With Achilleus considered invincible, the Trojans stayed away from him, while testing the ground outside the walls of Troy against other Achaian chiefs. Eventually, as soon as Achilleus appeared, the Trojans ran, inside the walls for their lives.

It has been nine years since the Achaians arrived on the coast of Troy. Each side, Trojans and Achaians, had learned to make the best of the situation. All the leaders and the heroes were given slave women captured from the valley. The two most beautiful of those women were Chryseis, the daughter of Chryse, priest of the Temple of Apollo, given to Agamemnon, and Briseis daughter of Brise, a farmer from near the fountain the Achaians used to get their water, who was given to Achilleus.

PART TWO:
Iliad

I. THE ANGER OF ACHILLEUS

A. The Chryseis' Incident.

Chryse, wearing a suppliant's wreath on his head and holding the scepter of Apollo, came to the Greek camp with ransom to plead for his daughter's return. "Son of Atreus and all Achaians" he begged, "I will pray to the gods to give you victory and guide you on the way home; please accept my ransom and return my daughter Chryseis to me for the sake of Apollo, son of Zeus." Agamemnon responded with harsh words,"Get away from me old man, and if I see you around again, neither your scepter nor your wreath will save you from my wrath. You will never get your daughter back. She will get old as my slave, by my side." Chryse obeyed, and walked away, heartbroken, toward the seashore. There he stopped, raised his hands and prayed to Apollo "Big god of the silver bow", he cried," if I ever sacrificed bulls and goats and burned the fat of their thighbones for your sake, make the Achaians pay for my tears with your arrows". Apollo heard his priest, and came down from Olympus, right across the camp of the Achaians, with his bow and his shining quiver, his angry face looking like the dark night. He immediately began shooting his arrows, first at the dogs and animals, and then at the men, themselves. For nine days and nights Apollo's arrows flew with clatter at the Achaians, and pestilence spread all over their camp. The smoke from the pyres of the dead rising towards the sky, could be seem from miles away.

On the tenth day Hera felt pity for the Greeks, and inspired Achilleus to call the Achaians into assembly. "Listen to me Achaians and you son of Atreus", Achilleus said, "between our war losses, and the pestilence, I think our chances of achieving our goal here are very slim. We will be lucky if we even stay alive long enough to return home. It is vital that we ask Calchas, wisest of soothsayers, to tell us why Apollo is so angry with us; is it possible we forgot to offer a hecatomb or to keep a promise we made to him?"

"Oh godly looking Achilleus", Seer Calchas answered, "I will tell you, if you first swear that you will protect me in case Agamemnon, son of Atreus is angered with what I have to say." Achilleus reassured him that as long as he lives he will make sure that no one, including Agamemnon, would dare touch him. Calchas then explained that Apollo is angry because his priest came to Agamemnon, with precious ransom to ask for the return of his daughter, who was his only support; but Agamemnon, not only refused, but was insolent to him and his office. "Apollo is not going to stop his punishment", he said, "until Chryseis is returned to her father; now, not only without a ransom, but also with a holy hecatomb to appease him".

Achilleus' hand went for his sword, when he felt a gentle touch on his hair.

When Agamemnon heard this, he jumped from his seat full of rage. "Malevolent Seer," he said, "every time you open your mouth you bring me grief. I want you to know that I love Chryseis because of her beauty and intelligence, I was looking forward to keeping her as my wife, but I am willing to let her go to save my people, provided that I am compensated by being given somebody else's slave.

Achilleus called Agamemnon selfish and said that he had no right to take a present already given, to someone else. "If that is the case," Agamemnon answered "I will come and take back the slave of my choice, from Ajax or Odysseus or you and see how you like it. But this can wait. For the present let us load a hecatomb on a ship with Chryseis in it going back to her father."

Achilleus snapped back at Agamemnon with equal furry. "I did not come here because the Trojans did me harm; I came to help you and the Greek cause. It turned out that every time a Trojan city was to be conquered it was me that had to do most of the fighting, while the Atreans managed to get the lion's share of the loot. The only thing left for me to do is take my ships and go back to Phthia, my country."

"I am not going to lose any sleep over you fleeing nor will I beg you to stay". Said Agamemnon, "I have plenty of fighters to honor me, and with Zeus' help, I will not need

Patroclus brought Achilleus' Briseis to the heralds, for the stubborn king.

you. You disgust me more than any other king; you only derive pleasure from fighting and blood. Even your bravery was not earned, but had to be given to you by your godly mother. To give you and any other disrespectful big mouth a lesson, soon as Chryseis is gone, I will come to your tent and take away your good looking slave, Briseis."

Now Achilleus had reached the boiling point, and his hand went for his sword, when he felt a gentle touch on his blonde hair. He turned and he was amazed by the brilliance of the face of Athena, whom he immediately recognized. "What are you doing here daughter of Zeus? he asked. "I was sent by Hera", she said, "to tell you not to draw your sword, and to say that whatever they take from you, you are destined to receive, later, as gifts three time their value." Achilleus pushed the hilt of his sword back into its scabbard as Athena disappeared. But he wasn't through with Agamemnon. He told him that he was swindling his people and that he had the face of a dog and the heart of a doe. Also, when Hector brings the best of the Achaians down, they are going to long for Achilleus, who will not be found.

Nestor, the respected king of Pylians, stood up and tried to calm things. "This is a sad day, when the best of the Achaians quarrel. Priam would have been delighted if he could hear you two. I suggest, before any more damage is done that Agamemnon changes his mind about taking Achilleus' prize, and Achilleus shows more respect for Agamemnon's rank. To this Agamemnon answered that he is sick and tired with Achilleus' thinking, that because gods gave him courage, he has the right to bne dis respectful. Achilleus said he would give up Briseis; but if Agamemnon tries to keep taking his prizes, his spear would get red with his blood.

With these last words the assembly ended. Agamemnon went to oversee the preparation of the ship for the return of Chryseis together with a hecatomb for Apollo, assigning Odysseus as captain of the ship. He also ordered all the Achaians to purify themselves for the sake of Apollo, by bathing in the sea. Achilleus then went back to his tent and ships.

Now that the matter of Chryseis was resolved, Agamemnon felt it was time to get satisfaction from Achilleus. So, he sent two heralds to take Briseis by the hand from Achilleus' tent. When Achilleus saw them he wasn't happy, but he held his composure, and spoke to them kindly. " Welcome, heralds of Zeus", he said, "I know why you are here and it is not your fault." Then, he instructed Patroclus to bring the girl out for the stubborn king.

B. Achilleus asks Thetis to arrange for Zeus to help the Trojans.

As soon as the heralds were gone, Achilleus left the tent and walked along the shore, looking at the foaming sea and crying. He raised his hands and begged, "Mother, who gave me life destined to be short, ask Zeus, the lord of Olympus, to turn a sympathetic glance at me and give me back the glory, the son of Atreus has tarnished by grabbing from me the prize, which I had worked so much for. Thetis heard her son from the depths of the ocean and jumped out of the waves with a spray. "My precious child, why are you weeping? What sorrow breaks your heart, please tell me." "Why should I repeat things you already know?", Achilleus responded. Then, he felt the need to talk and went over the whole story about Chryseis and Briseis. He added, "I would be glad to see the Trojans helped by Zeus to push the Achaians all the way to their ships".

"Don't worry my son", his mother said, "I will go to Olympus to help you get satisfaction and happiness for the rest of your remaining life.

In the mean time, Odysseus with Chryseis and a hecatomb, reached Apollo's temple where Chryse was thankful to have his daughter back. A ceremony was immediately arranged for the sake of Apollo. The sacrificial animals were set around the altar; then all participants washed their hands and sprinkled the animals with barley, while Chryse thanked Apollo and said there was no reason for punishing the Achaians any further. Apollo heard his priest and halted his deadly arrows against the Achaians.

Thetis pleads with Zeus to help her son Achilleus, by favoring the Trojans.

While the Achaians were to get relief from Apollo's arrows, their woes were not over. For just about that time Thetis was coming out of the waves to go to Mount Olympus to see Zeus. She found Zeus sitting on one of the peaks of the mountain, and she went and knelt in front of him. With tears in her eyes, she hugged his knees and said, "Father, if I have honored you with words and deeds, I beg you help my son in his short life find happiness and satisfaction, by making the Trojans victorious over the Achaians, so that Agamemnon honors him to the extend he deserves."

Zeus listened but said nothing. So, Thetis continued, "If the answer is "NO", tell me, so I can understand that I am the most inferior of the gods. Zeus, nodded his head and said, "You know you are getting me in trouble with Hera and you also know, I never take back a promise after I nod my head." With these words they parted. Thetis went back to her bright palace in the kingdom of the sea; while Zeus joined the other gods where they were sitting. All the gods rose as he appeared. Hera had not missed what took place between Zeus and silver footed Thetis, and she didn't like it. "I know you cheated behind my back again, I know you promised to give glory to Achilleus by having the Trojans batter the Achaians." Zeus replied that when he wanted her to know about something he would tell her; otherwise, she must not pry, if she knew what was best for her. "You really won't like to see me get angry", he added. Hera understood it was time to stop. Hephaestus tried to help, "You two should really not be fighting for the sake of mortals," he said, and offered his mother Hera a drink of nectar from a golden cup he had made for her. "Mother, you know I love you, and I hate to see you sad; but please stop going after father because I wouldn't like to see you get hurt. Last time I tried to help you, he picked me up by the leg and tossed me with such force I traveled all day before I fell on the island of Lemnos. My leg felt dead; I didn't think I would ever be able to walk again. Hera smiled and drank the nectar from the golden cup. Hephaestus, then went around offering sweet nectar to all the gods, who knew it was time for a feast. Apollo played his magic harp while the muses sang; then they all enjoyed sweet sleep 'till the next morning; except Zeus, who was busy planning ways to give honor to Achilleus.

C. Zeus tricks Agamemnon in his dream to order general attack.

Zeus came up with a scheme to have Hypnos, the deceitful god of dreams, appear in Agamemnon's dream disguised as King Nestor, and tell him that Zeus, and the rest of the gods agree for the Achaians to capture Troy, if they were to attack now. Agamemnon, immediately understood this was his opportunity to show he did not need Achilleus and lost no time in setting things in motion. As Dawn drew the veils of the night from Olympus and the rest of the world, he first called for a meeting of the council of elders. They concluded that the dream was significant and that they should act on it. He immediately sent out the heralds to announce a general assembly. Before long, there was a tremendous commotion outside, as fifty thousand warriors left their ships, like bees swarming from an underground cave. The earth quivered under the pounding of their feet as the men moved to find their place. Nine heralds cried for them to quiet down so that the kings could be heard. Finally Agamemnon spoke, "My proud friends, Zeus has assured me the time has come to go sack the city of Priam. For the past nine years we have been fighting here. We have persisted because we wouldn't want to return to our homes dishonored, without accomplishing what we came here for. Would you want to return home empty handed after the loss of so many of our heroic brothers, when we number ten times the warriors of Troy?" "Yes," they all cried, "we will be happy to go back to our wives and children, and the hell with the victory at Troy." Agamemnon whose job was supposed to inspire his warriors to battle, was stunned and ready to give in to the will of his constituents. Hera, who was listening from the top of Mt Olympus was alarmed with the turn of events and sent Athena to the rescue disguised as a herald. She first spoke to Odysseus. "Noble son of Laertes, she said, "are you going to also run away with the ships, giving Priam and the Trojans the glory of keeping Helen, or are you going to say something to straighten the minds of the crowd?" Odysseus, who recognized Athena, ran to see Agamemnon, who was standing there, dumfounded. "It is not time to abandon our struggle, we must think like mature people, we have sacrificed too much, and we are just about at the point where, according to Sear Calchas' prophesy, Troy is supposed to fall in the ninth year, which is now." The Achaian warriors who knew Odysseus, and with the help of Athena standing next to him, immediately started changing their thinking. The highly respected King Nestor, then, continued along the same line; "Achaians, you must stop talking like children, for you are now grown up men and know what war and obligations mean. You Agamemnon will be our chief and if anyone dares flee, he may as well meet his death dishonorably right there." Agamemnon agreed and ordered, as soon as dinner was to be over, that everyone prepare for tomorrow's battle; sharpen his sword and spear, and inspect his shield, get ready to fight for a whole day. Then he ordered the sacrifice of a five year old bull for Zeus' sake and invited the heroes, Ajax, Idomeneus, Odysseus, and Menelaos to participate. Many animals were slaughtered and cooked on the fires to provide everybody with a good dinner.

In the next morning, the heralds cried for each fighter to assemble with his own group near his ship. Agamemnon gave the order and men, horses, and chariots started marching towards Troy. Agamemnon counted on a surprise attack on Troy; but you couldn't trust the gods those days. Zeus sent Iris, messenger of the gods, to inform the Trojans of the impeding attack. She found Priam and Hector in a meeting, where she entered disguised as Priam's son Politis, who had been placed guard to watch for the Achaians at the tallest tower. "They are here", he said, "so many, the plain is covered with men, like milk infested with flies." Hector jumped up to run out of the room. With the fighters for Troy on a continuous alert, it didn't take long before the Trojans and their allies assembled, the doors to swing wide open, and for Hector with the thousands of armed men to be out in the plane. They did not have to travel far to encounter the Achaians. Now they could recognize most of the leaders, each backed by his own men. Before long the two armies were facing each other, determined to fight to the death.

III. PARIS IS OUT TO FIGHT

Hector was surprised to see Paris in the front, next to him, actually challenging the Achaian leaders to a fight. He was tall and well built, wearing a panther's skin and holding two spears, while his bow was hanging from his shoulder; but as a fighter he was unknown to the Achaians so he was not getting any eager opponent. That is, until Menelaos spotted him. It was like a dream had come true. Menelaos jumped from his chariot and ran straight for Paris. When Paris saw him coming, he became pale and started trembling, as if he was facing a dangerous snake and he ran for his life to hide among the Trojan fighters. Hector was quick to scold him. "Poor Paris, handsome and a womanizer, but too much of a coward to stand like a man; It would have been better if you were never born or died unmarried instead of bringing shame and disaster to your family. It would have been better than being disgraced and mocked upon. Won't the Achaians mock us and say the one we sent to defend us looks like a lion but has the heart of a jack rabbit? You went abroad and snatched a beautiful married woman, but now you don't dare face and find out whose wife that woman was. Your lyre and your well combed curls wouldn't help you with your mouth in the dust before him." Paris, still pale and humiliated, answered, "While you are right my brother, remember we don't refuse god's gifts. The gods gave you courage, and Aphrodite gave me my precious woman for whom I am willing to die. Arrange it for me to fight Menelaos alone, while the Trojans and Achaians sit and watch. Whoever wins takes Helen and her treasures; while Trojans and Achaians leave in peace."

A. The Two Sides Agree to a Truce, and Let the Outcome Be Determined by a Single Combat Between Paris and Menelaos.

Hector was pleased. He walked in front of the Trojan phalanx, holding his spear in the middle and high up in the air, a signal to his soldiers to hold back. They understood and stopped, but the Achaians kept aiming stones and arrows at him, until Agamemnon, understood Hector wanted to speak and shouted for everybody to stop and listen. "Hear me Trojans and Achaians," Hector said, " Paris has asked me to propose that you all lay your arms down on the ground, while he and Menelaos alone fight it out in single combat. Whoever wins takes Helen and her wealth, while Trojans and Achaians, thereafter, live in peace." Menelaos, who was disappointed having to lose Paris in combat was being given a second chance. He immediately stood up waving his hands, "Listen to me who is the most aggrieved, I agree to fight with Paris, who has been the cause of all this. Whoever falls, let him die, while the rest of you, who have suffered so much, fight no more. Troy, being the proposing side, will bring a white ram for the Earth and a black ewe for the Sun; while the Achaians offer a ram to Zeus. We will also need Priam to validate the treaty, as we really do not trust his young sons to uphold the pledge."

Iris went to Helen disguised as her sister-in-law Laodice, the prettiest of Priam's daughters, and told her about the agreement accepted by both sides. "Come see Helen, the Achaians and Trojans are sitting down with their armor next to them" she said, as she was pulling Helen toward the Scaean tower Gates. At the gates she found several old men, including Priam, who invited Helen to sit down in front of him. He told her that he does not blame her, but the gods, for what has happened. Then he asked her to identify Agamemnon, Odysseus and Ajax, and she did. She also pointed out that the god-looking fellow next to huge Ajax, was Idomeneus, king of the Cretans.

In the mean time the heralds from Troy had brought in the lambs and a goatskin full of wine for the sacrifice. Priam left to attend the armistice ceremony. He rode a chariot with his friend Antenor to near the spot where the chiefs had gathered, then he dismounted and proceeded on foot. Agamemnon and Odysseus both rose as he approached. The armistice oath ceremony could now start.

The heralds mixed wine from the goatskin with water into a mixing bowl, then poured water for the chiefs participating in the ceremony to wash their hands. Agamemnon clipped hair from the head of each of the lambs and gave it to the heralds to distribute to the participating chiefs of both armies, then he raised his hands and prayed. "Glorious Zeus of mount Ida, and dazzling Sun, who sees everything and hears all oaths, fertile mother Earth, smoothly flowing Rivers, and god of the underworld, witness our agreement and punish whomever breaks the armistice oath. We promise that if Paris kills Menelaos, he can keep Helen and her wealth; but if the opposite happens, the Trojans, besides surrendering Helen and her possessions, will also pay compensation to the Achaians, for the insult and their suffering." As he was speaking his last words, he pulled his knife and slashed the throats of each of the animals. Both Greek and Trojan chiefs then filled their cups with wine from the mixing bowl and poured it to show the gods they agreed with the oath. Parts of the oath others repeated, sometimes adding to it like, "Let those, who break the oaths, meet death and as this red wine is spilled let their brains be spilled on the ground and their wives find servitude." But, the oaths and prayers did not agreed with Zeus' plans, so, he disregarded them. Priam went back to Troy, for he did not feel strong enough to witness the fight.

Meanwhile, Paris and Menelaos were preparing for the fight. When they were ready, the signal was given by the heralds and they started walking towards each other until they were very close. First Paris threw his spear at Menelaos, that hardly pierced the thick buffalo skin of his shield. Then Menelaos, while praying to father Zeus and gathering all his strength, hurled his spear at Paris, that penetrated Paris shield and tore through his tunic. Paris had swerved to the side so he only got a superficial wound at his flank, and escaped death. Menelaos, pulled his sharp sword and came down with a strong blow on the top of Paris helmet. The sword broke into several pieces. Menelaos, in his frenzy, found himself silently talking to the gods, "Cruel Zeus, why don't you hear my prayers? I have been injured enough already, yet you take away my weapons when this scoundrel deserves to die? He leaped and grabbed Paris by the crest of his helmet and dragged him toward the Achaian's side. Paris couldn't resist as he was being choked by his chin strap and wouldn't have lasted much longer if it wasn't for Aphrodite, who broke the strap, covered him in a cloud

Menelaos and Paris in single combat.

and moved him comfortably to his chamber in Troy. Menelaos was left holding Paris helmet, which he threw away and ran to find Paris amongst the Trojan ranks. The Trojans made no effort to stop him, as they felt dishonored by Paris running away from the arranged combat.

Aphrodite, disguised as one of her maids, went to get Helen, to go join Paris. Helen took one look at her and new who she was. "What do you want from me now, satanic goddess, what evil thoughts are you entertaining in your head?", Helen asked. "Nothing", Aphrodite answered, "I only think that your place is next to your husband right now." After Paris' fiasco with Menelaos, Helen thought she would be the mock of the Trojan women, so she gave an angry look to Aphrodite. "Don't you dare provoke me hussy", Aphrodite said, "for I can hate as strongly as I can love. I can set Trojans and Achaians, at each other's throats, and a harrowing death for you, even though I love you. Helen was frightened and followed the goddess to Paris chamber. She found Paris lying on the bed clean and calm, as if he had just returned from a ball. "Well, here you are", Helen said, "poor Menelaos must be dying for you to be here. Or did he feel sorry for you and let you go? Do you still think you can face Menelaos? If so why don't you get up and go finish the fight you started?" "You are

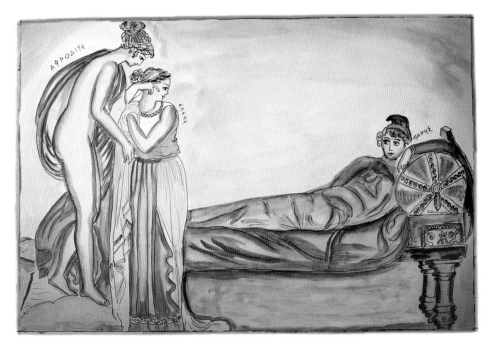

"I think your place is with your husband right now", Aphrodite told Helen.

being hard on me", Paris said, "I think it was Athena that helped Menelaos today; but the day may come for me yet. Why don't you come to me now and tell me instead that you love me?" "I am sorry", she said, "I apologize, I did not mean it. I wouldn't bear to see another combat between you and Menelaos." she said, as she was climbing into the bed, with Paris.

After Menelaos gave up looking for Paris, Agamemnon spoke again, "Trojans, and Trojan allies, I declare as a victor of the fight, the terms of which we all agreed, to be Menelaos. We, therefore, expect you to keep your end of the bargain: return Helen with all her possessions, and pay the fine we agreed upon!

III. ATHENA, APOLLO AND ARES MANAGE TO GET INVOLVED IN THE FIGHT

On top of Mt. Olympus the gods were relaxing, drinking nectar from golden cups. Zeus decided to have fun kidding Hera, "I only saw Aphrodite save Paris down there, what happened to you and Athena, how come you weren't there helping Menelaos? I can't understand what Troy has done, for you two to want her destruction, when there is no other city in the world that I love more?" "The cities I love", said Hera, "are Sparta, Argos and Mycenae; but if you want to destroy them, go ahead, I can't stop you, you being so much stronger than me. Remember though, I am also Cronus daughter, which makes me both your sister and your wife; so we should compromise. Send Athena to convince a Trojan to shoot at the Achaians to break the truce, and then, let them fight it out, with us watching. Zeus nodded, and Athena flew to the Trojan ranks disguised as Leodocus, son of Antenor. She found Pandarus, standing with other heroes. "This is your chance Pandarus" she said, "to become famous by finishing Paris' job and killing Menelaos; then he won't be around to claim himself a winner." The sharp archer Pandarus put an arrow next to the bowstring, he pulled and let go. The arrow flew straight at Menelaos' heart, but Athena diverted it enough to hit his belt, instead. It went through it, the point wounding him superficially. Black blood started oozing from the wound. Agamemnon was frantic. He called in Asclepius' son Machaon, the best doctor in the ranks, who pulled the arrow out and he sucked a mouthful of blood from the wound to prevent infection. He then applied herbs for the pain and healing. In the mean time, the soldiers of both sides were fast rearming and throwing arrows at each other. Agamemnon raised his head up high and said, "The Trojans broke their oath of armistice and attached us. Zeus will not let such scoundrels go unpunished; but we will take Troy and the vultures will tear the bodies of the liars, while we will be taking their wives and their children to our ships."

The Trojans for a moment thought they had the upper hand, and their leaders encouraged them to drive forward. Several Greeks were killed. With Achilleus absent, Agamemnon started calling on each of the other Achaian heroes, Idomeneus, Diomed, the Ajaxes and Odysseus, by name, to fight back. They all jumped into the battle and as they were all known to be dreaded killers, they were immediately noticed by the Trojans in front of them, who started retreating towards the walls. Many Trojans lost their lives as they were running for safety. Apollo, was very disturbed to see the Trojans flee in disorder. "Trojans," he cried, "hit the enemy, they don't have skin made of stone or iron, find out how easy it is to hurt them. You don't have to be afraid of Achilleus anymore, he remains in his ship and is no longer fighting." The Trojan soldiers were encouraged and turned around to counterattack the Achaians with vigor.

The Achaians immediately came under pressure and started retreating while they were defending themselves. The Trojan front was straightened, in line with the battalions of Hector and Aeneas who not only had withstood the Achaian attacks, but also had inflicted serious losses among brave Achaians. Pandarus, sent a fast arrow at Diomed, that penetrated his armor into his shoulder. Blood started oozing through his cuirass (leather breast plate). He stopped and had a comrade pull the arrow out. Then, all of a sudden, he felt better and strong as a lion, for It was Athena who had stimulated him. He jumped back on his chariot and went looking for Pandarus, while engaging and killing anyone in his way. Four brave Trojans, two of them sons of

Aphrodite saves and carries away her son Aeneas from Diomed's spear.

Priam, were struck down as if they were hit by lightning. When Pandarus saw him coming, he was terrified and called on Aeneas, son of Aphrodite, to protect him. Aeneas first asked him why was he not protecting himself with his bow. Pandarus said it was futile since a god must be protecting Diomed from his arrows. Aeneas then asked him to drive his chariot while he fights with Diomed.

Iris was quick to pick up and carry the wounded goddess to Olympus. As they were climbing up from the battlefield they met fierce Ares sitting on a cloud, waiting for his sister. Aphrodite fell on her knees in front of him begging, "Dear brother" she said, "I am badly wounded by a mortal, please let me borrow your horses to take me to Mt. Olympus fast." Ares obliged and she flew up with Iris on his chariot to the Olympus in good time. There, she let the horses loose and gave them ambrosial food to eat. She was pleasantly surprised to see her mother Dione running to her with open arms. "Which of the gods did this to you ?", her mother asked, as she was wiping the ichor pouring out of Aphrodite's hand. "It was a mortal, mother, proud Diomed", said the laughter loving goddess. "In this war, not even gods are safe. I only wanted to protect my child Aeneas from death", Aphrodite added. "We, up here on Olympus," Dione said, "suffer a lot from the hands of the mortals, but often we, ourselves cause

Iris was quick to pick up and carry the wounded goddess to Olympus.

pain to each other. We just have to bear it", Dione concluded; but then, she continued, "Wasn't Ares bound and kept in a bronze tank for three months by Otus and Ephialtes, until Hermes set him free? And didn't the son of Amphiitryon wound Hera with an arrow on her right breast and Pluto on his shoulder, and they both suffered terribly until Olympus' doctor Paeeon healed them by applying herbs on their wounds? When a mortal wounds any of us death finds him soon, so Diomed's wife should Know, she will soon be the widow of a brave man."

As Dione kept caressing her daughter, and while she spoke, the pain in Aphrodite's hand was being lifted away, until she was healed. Hera and Athena felt satisfaction for Aphrodite's misfortune. "She probably tried to match a Greek woman with a

Trojan hero, and got her hand caught in the woman's breastpin," Athena said. Zeus smiled and called golden Aphrodite to sit next to him. "My beautiful Aphrodite, you were not made for battlefields, go take care of your love duties and leave war to Ares, Enyo and Athena," Zeus said. Aphrodite just smiled.

On the Trojan front, the battle continued to rage. The chiefs of the Achaians and the Trojans kept encouraging their men to battle. On the Achaian side, Agamemnon, Menelaos, the two Ajaxes, Idomeneus, and of course Diomed. On the Trojan side Hector, Sarpedon and the gods Ares, Enyo, and Apollo. Ares was the most destruc-

The Horas opened the gates of heaven to Athena's carriage.

tive, for he kept using his spear repeatedly each time piercing a brave fighter. Hera up on Mt. Olympus was dismayed. She asked Athena's help and she did not refuse. They both mounted Athena's chariot and flew through the clouds towards the battlefield.

They saw Zeus sitting on the highest peak of Olympus, and Hera spoke to him, "Father Zeus, aren't you angry with the way Ares is behaving? Would you have any objection if I hit him hard enough to push him out of the Battle?" Zeus replied, "Have Athena do that, for she knows how to punish him better than anyone else." That is all they wanted to hear; now they had Zeus' permission. When they arrived at the point where the rivers Simois and Scamander meet, they dismounted. Hera hid the horses in a cloud and ordered Simois to grow ambrosia for them to eat. Then they both flew like birds to the spot where the Achaians were retreating fast as they were hard pressed by the Trojans, counterattacking. Hera shouted with a voice of fifty men, "Shame on you Achaians, able to accomplish nothing without Achilleus. Unless you stand up to them now, they will push you all the way to your ships." Her words revived their hearts and souls and the retreat ended. Athena jumped next to Diomed who had stopped to cool his wound from Pandarus' arrow, as the belt of his shield was digging into his wound, causing it to bleed and become irritated. "Your father

Athena took the reins and whip from Diomed and drove straight at Ares.

wouldn't have bothered with a little wound like that," Athena said, "or do you find it as an excuse to keep out of the battle?" "I recognize you, daughter of Aegis-bearing Zeus, I am not afraid to fight and I follow your advice.

I did not hesitate wounding goddess Aphrodite, but when it comes to confronting dangerous gods like Ares and Apollo, I try to stay away", he answered. "Diomed, son of Tydeus," she said, "don't be afraid of Ares or any other immortal, for I will be on your side." With that, she lifted Sthenelus, Diomed's companion, who found himself falling from the chariot and rolling on the ground. She put on the helmet, given to her by Pluto to make herself invisible; then she positioned herself next to Diomed, she took the reins and whip from Diomed's hands, and drove the horses straight toward Ares. Ares was busy stripping Periphas, a brave Aetolian, whom he had just killed. He was jubilant to see Diomed coming within range of his spear and was sure of an easy kill. He threw his bronze spear over the reins and yoke aiming at Diomed's heart; but Athena deflected the spear over the chariot. It was now Diomed's turn to throw his spear at Ares. This time Athena drove the spear into Ares stomach. Ares roared like ten thousand men getting wounded at the same time, and both Achaians and Trojans panicked. From where Ares stood, Diomed saw a dark cloud rising fast into the heaven and Ares flew straight to Mt. Olympus.

Although Ares didn't see Athena, he was sure it was her doing, for no mortal would

Ares felt totally rejuvenated, after Hebe bathed and clothed him

have dared attack him alone. He went and sat next to Zeus and showed him his wound. "Father Zeus", he said, how can you not be angry at the bitch who happens to be your daughter? Had I stayed there longer, she probably would have finished me, altogether. But Zeus was not sympathetic and gave him an angry look. "You know I hate whining", he said, "you cause me more aggravation than all the gods on Mt. Olympus; You are as obnoxious as your mother Hera from where you probably have inherited your nastiness. If you weren't my son, I would send you to keep company with the Titans long time ago. But being my own flesh and ichor have Paeeon soothe and heal your wound. Paeeon, doctor of the gods, obeyed Zeus wishes and cured the nasty Ares instantly. Ares then felt refreshed and totally rejuvenated after Hebe bathed and clothed him.

IV. HECTOR TAKES TIME OUT OF FIGHTING TO VISIT TROY

The loss of Aeneas and Ares from the battle had a profound effect on both ranks, the Achaians were encouraged and the Trojans were feeling the pressure. Hector suspected the finger of Athena, and decided to go to Troy and offer a sacrifice in her Temple. By the Scaean gates he saw a crowd of women, running towards him, to ask about their husbands, sons and other relatives. To some he said go home and cry. To the rest he suggested they go and pray to Athena.

"You are here brooding while our people perish", Hector shouted at Paris.

Hector then walked towards the polished colonnade which adorned Priam's luxurious palace. Besides the main building, where Priam and Hecuba resided, the palace extended to a complex of two lines of chambers separated by a courtyard. One line encompassed fifty chambers for Priam's sons and their wives; while twelve chambers were built across the courtyard for Priam's daughters and their husbands. The palace was filled with excitement as the women rushed to greet Hector. His mother ran to him accompanied by Laodice, one of his beautiful sisters; she took his hands in her's. "My son, she said, is everything alright? ordinarily I wouldn't expect you to leave the battleground without a reason. Let me offer you some wine so you can make an offering to the immortals and then drink to get refreshed." "Mother," he answered, "please don't bring me any wine for I must keep a clear head. Besides, I couldn't make an offering to the gods with my blood-stained hands, I must be thoroughly washed. I suggest you gather your ladies and bring an offering to the temple of Athena; bring the most beautiful gown in your wardrobe and place it on the knees of her image. Then you sacrifice ten young oxen, each less than a year old. For we need her to take pity on Troy and stop Diomed, who fights with such fury, he has caused panic throughout the Trojan army. Hecuba understood Troy had a crisis, and she went to execute Hector's instructions, exactly as he suggested, as soon as her son left. But Athena ignored Hecuba's offerings.

"My darling wife, I must fight, to postpone the day you lose your freedom"

Hector next entered Paris' home, which he had built for him with the best artisans in the land near Priam's and his own house on the Acropolis. He entered holding his long spear. Paris was busy fixing his armor and a new spear. "You are here brooding your anger", Hector shouted at Paris, "while our people perish under the spears of the Achaeans. We need everyone's help or it won't be long before you see our city in a blaze." Paris first listened without saying a word; then finally he decided to answer, "Hector," he said, "I understand, but I am not here because I am angry at anyone, but because I am depressed. In fact Helen was talking to me hinting that it is time for me to go to battle. You can wait for me, or go ahead and I will catch up with you." Helen spoke next and she also sounded very depressed. Then she asked Hector to sit, but he refused. "If you want to do me a favor", he said, persuade your husband to overtake me."

Hector left Paris' house in a hurry because he was anxious to see his wife Andromache and his adorable son whom he had named Scamandrius, but the people called Astyanax, Prince of the City . He quickly walked to his house where the house-keeper told him his wife had heard the Trojans were badly pressed by the Achaians and had run up the high wall to see what was happening. He decided he had no time to go look for her; but as he was exiting the Scaean gates to go back to the plain, he saw Andromache running toward him. Behind her the nurse was running with the boy. The boy apparently did not recognize his father with the tall helmet and bloody hands and he started crying. Andromache took Hector's hands in hers with tears in her eyes. "My dear husband", she said, your bravery will be the end of you. Think of your son without a father and think of me to be a widow, without any relative left in this world, for you are now to me husband, brother father and mother. My father, king of Thebes, was killed by Achilleus long time ago and my mother was brought by Artemis to Priam's house where she died. Please stay within the walls for our sake." And Hector answered, "My darling wife, don't you think I know what you say, that my heart aches for my family? But how can I look at the face of the men and women of Troy if they think of me be a coward? As it is, it is difficult to defend the city, which someday will probably fall to the Achaians and Priam and my mother and people will perish. But nothing grieves me more than the thought of you weeping as you will be carried by a copper covered Achaian to his ship. Who knows which loom awaits you in Argos or from which spring you will have to carry water for a mistress. If that happens I want them to remember that you were wife to Hector, the commander in chief and a fighter. I want to postpone the day you lose your freedom; but if that day ever comes, I prefer to be buried-ashes underground than hearing your cry as they take you to captivity." He stretched to pick up his son, but the child withdrew hugging the neck of his lovely nurse. The parents laughed. Hector then took off his helmet, and placed his spear on the ground; the child recognized his father and stretched his arms to him. Hector picked and kissed his son and he cradled him in his arms. He turned his eyes towards the sky and prayed to Zeus for his son to grow even stronger than him and make his mother happy. Then he handed his son over to his wife and caressed both of them. "Don't worry," he said, "I know how to defend myself, nothing will happen to me unless the gods so decide. Go home, get busy with your loom and keep the bad thoughts out of your head!" He put on his helmet, took his spear and walked toward the battlefield. Andromache started for home, crying hysterically and turning back her head from time to time, to look at Hector; she knew this was the last time she was to see him alive, and started mourning for him already.

Paris was walking in the same direction and he slowed down his pace for Hector to catch up. "I am happy to see you here" Hector said, "we need brave fighters like you. The Trojans have not done justice to you. Let us make things right between ourselves."

V. HECTOR FIGHTS HUGE AJAX IN SINGLE COMBAT

The return of Hector and Paris encouraged the Trojan ranks to start a new attack against the Achaians, who within minutes were retreating in disorder, not too far from their ships. Hector felt confident and announced that he was ready to fight the best Achaian in single combat. Nine heroes volunteered from the Greek side and lots were drawn to pick one. It was huge Ajax who was selected, as all the Achaians were hoping. The combatants walked cautiously toward each other. "I will show you the

The heralds stop the single combat between Huge Ajax and Hector.

kind of men Greeks raise." said Ajax, and Hector replied that he was experienced enough in combat to kill him with just using tricks, but he said he will not do that and will win with his strength. With those words he hurled his spear at Ajax that only penetrated six of the seven layers of Ajax's huge shield. Ajax's spear then went through Hector's shield, tore his tunic and slightly wounded his neck, drawing some blood. Hector was shaken, but undeterred. He picked a rugged rock and threw it at Ajax, who had no difficulty deflecting it with his shield. Now it was Ajax's turn, with a rock as big as a mill-stone. Hector staggered backwards as the rock hit and broke his shield; he would have fallen on the ground if Apollo had not held him up. Both combatants then drew their swords, ready to finish the other when the two heralds intervened. "With the consent of both of you, we suggest that the fight be stopped as it is getting too dark." Both fighters agreed to stop.

48

As a token of admiration for each other, they agreed to exchange presents. Hector gave Ajax a sword in a silver scabbard, and Ajax gave Hector his belt, beautifully decorated in purple. A truce was declared soon after, to take away the dead from the battlefield.

VI. ZEUS FORBIDS INTERVENTION BY THE GODS, VISITS MT. IDA OVERLOOKING THE BATTLEFIELD.

Zeus was content with the way events were going, but he was not yet satisfied that he had fulfilled his promise to Thetis. He called a meeting of all the gods at the highest peak of Olympus. "Listen to me gods and goddesses", he said, "I don't want any of you intervene anymore on either side of the Trojan war. If anyone dares disobey me, I will punish him or her severely; I may even throw him or her down to dark Tartarus with the bronze floors and iron doors, as deep down as the surface of the earth is below the sky. And if you doubt that I am strong enough to talk this way, I challenge you to try and find out. Give me one end of a gold chain, and at the other end you all join together to bring me down from heaven to earth; you will not succeed, while I can pull all of you, tie the chain around one of the peaks of Olympus, and let you dangle there, forever. The gods remained silent. Then Athena looked at her father with a smile and said, "Father, you don't have to tell us how strong you are, but can we, at least, feel sorry for the poor Greeks, and perhaps advise them from time to time of how to avert total destruction?" "Come on" Zeus said, "you are taking me too seriously, and you know how I feel about you." With these words, he mounted his golden carriage with his fleet footed horses; with the sound of his golden whip, the horses leaped forward in the sky taking Zeus to the top of Mount Ida, overlooking the Trojan battleground. The Trojans couldn't have hoped for a better windfall.

Fighting started early that morning. The Greeks were still eating breakfast when they saw the Trojan chariots racing toward them. Behind, them marched the whole Trojan infantry. It was clear that Hector had decided to quickly defeat the Greeks and save the women and children of Troy. The Greeks, who were already armed, assembled in a hurry and the two armies advanced at each other. They met with a loud clatter as bronze shields and spears clashed; then, there was the uproar from the cries of triumph, despair, pain and dying that filled the air, as blood was flowing onto the prairie. Zeus was rejoicing for having a first class seat to watch the battle, and for his victory with the immortals earlier in the morning. Zeus took out of his pocket the golden scale with the Greek Death Fate in one pan and the Trojan Death Fate in the other. First he let the scale balance; then he gave a fierce look at the Greek side, that made it sink all the way to the ground. Immediately, black clouds gathered and lighting and thunderbolts fell on the Achaian army! Idomeneus' and Agamemnon's men started retreating. Nestor was holding for awhile, when Paris killed one of his horses and the others were confused. Hector drove his chariot for a kill. When Diomed saw what was happening he called on Odysseus, who was running toward the ships, to help. Odysseus ignored the plea, so Diomed ran to Nestor and took him aboard his chariot, thus saving him from sure death. Nestor took the reins while Diomed cast a javelin towards Hector's chariot; he missed Hector, but killed Eniopeus, his charioteer. Hector had a difficult time to retrieve the reins to drive away to replace his charioteer. Three times Diomed tried to chase Hector but each time thunderbolts flashed in front of his chariot and his horses went wild. Nestor recognized Zeus work and advised Diomed to retreat, which he did reluctantly as Hector was screaming at him,"Diomed son of Tydeus, the Achaians are bragging about you being brave, but I think you are a woman. You will never get our women and children, while I am around; instead, it will be me that will determine your fate."

A. Athena and Hera Ride Again, Despite Zeus Warning

Hera was so angry with Hector's boasting, that she was bouncing on her throne with rage and all of Olympus was jumping. Then she had an idea, call Poseidon, the strongest god after Zeus. "Powerful earth shaker", she said, "how can your heart not ache for the poor Greeks who are being killed like flies? Weren't they the ones who were sacrificing and burning delicious animal legs covered with fat for your nose?" "Big mouth Hera", he responded, "what are you talking about, you know that even if all of you were to agree with me, I still couldn't fight Zeus, for he is far mightier than all of us." It was a good try, Hera thought, now what? At this point even a band aid would help. She went into Agamemnon's thoughts that he would inspire the chiefs to resist to the end to avert catastrophe. And Agamemnon did so; he called each king by name and told him how important it was to fight hard. But the Trojan attack continued and his bravest fighters were already wounded. Hera was desperate; she met with Athena, who she knew shared her views and had the guts to fight. "It is a shame we allow the destruction of the Greeks, by this lunatic Hector, son of Priam", she said. "I agree", said Athena, "Hector deserves to die, but I blame my father, who is full of mischief. Now, my father is mad at me, while he grants Thetis' wishes to honor Achilleus, just because she touches his knees and pets his beard. He forgot that it was me who helped his son Hercules and saved him from death. We have no alternative but to go down there and see how much Hector will be delighted to see us. You can get the horses ready, while I put on my armor". Within seconds the flaming chariot with the two goddesses was going through the gates of heaven. Zeus couldn't believe his eyes. He knew he had to remain tough if he was to continue to be respected; but disciplining his wife and daughter and upsetting the family, he hated to do. He decided to send goddess Iris to go and scare them to return to Olympus. Iris knew her job. "The son of Cronus wants you to come back," she said, "if you don't, you will see your chariot broken to pieces, underneath you, horses and all." Hera and Athena agreed that subjecting themselves to this kind of danger for the sake of mortals was too much and gave up the expedition. As the two goddesses conversed, the Achaians were being pushed behind their wall. If they were to lose that, next their ships would be in danger.

Soon after, Zeus got on his chariot and drove back to Olympus, where he sat on his golden throne. The other gods gathered around, for they all expected to see some excitement. Hera's seat, next to Zeus' throne remained empty. Hera went and sat further down, next to Athena. They both had long faces. "Hey you two, why do you look so angry, did you get tired of killing Trojans? You really got away with murder today and you were lucky I didn't let you taste some of my lightening." For awhile, none of them said a word; then Hera answered, "You don't have to keep reminding us of how mighty you are Zeus. But, you must realize, somebody here should show a little compassion for the poor Greeks who perish every day. We don't battle for them, we only advise them how to save themselves." "You do that, my dear wife," Zeus answered, "and you are going to see me tomorrow morning causing the death of thousands of Achaians; for it is my decree that Hector will not stop his attack until he draws Achilleus to the battlefield." Hera kept quiet.

B. Agamemnon ready to give up, offers fortune to appease Achilleus.

At nightfall, the battle subsided to the relief of the fighters who welcomed the chance to rest. The chiefs welcomed the opportunity to think. Agamemnon, greatly discouraged, sent the heralds out to call the chiefs to council. The chiefs were disheartened because of their losses and retreats, and were curious to hear Agamemnon's thoughts. When all were present, Agamemnon, very emotional with tears in his eyes, announced that he had decided their chances of ever defeating Troy were remote and that they should pack up and go home. "Son of Atreus," Diomed demanded, "go home, if you cannot stand the pressure of war, but the rest of us will stay and occupy Troy." Nestor then suggested that Agamemnon, who was the high king in the campaign, was still young and should have listened to him when he suggested to leave Briseis alone, instead of angering Achilleus. He further proposed there may still be time to soften Achilleus heart with a lot of presents and smart talk. Agamemnon admitted he was wrong and that he was ready to reconsider his harsh actions toward Achilleus. "I was crazy to hurt godly Achilleus and risk Zeus' punishment. I am now willing to pay him back for my lunacy. I will give him seven new cooking tripods, thee talents worth of gold, 20 kettles, and his woman Briseis back, unscathed. I will also give him seven of the beautiful girls we captured at the island of Lesvos, who are experts on the loom and knitting. In addition, I will give him twelve thoroughbred horses that have won a fortune for me. And when we get to Troy let him load his ship with gold and silver and twenty women of his choice. Finally, if we ever get back to our country he can become my son-in-law by choosing anyone of my three beautiful daughters, with seven of my cities as a dowry present." Everyone recognized there was a lot of value in Agamemnon's offerings. Without wasting time they all agreed and sent an envoy to Achilleus consisting of Phoenix, a mentor of Achilleus during his youth, the great Ajax,

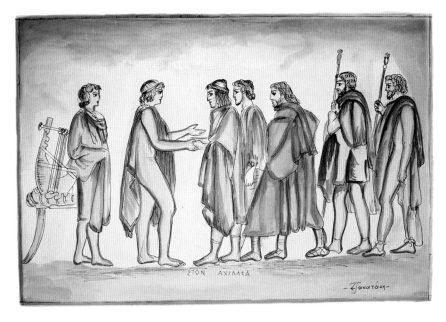

Achilleus refuses to sell his pride for whatever the fortune offered.

and the ingenious Odysseus, together with the two most distinguished heralds. Before leaving, all members of the envoy washed their hands to pray to Zeus.

Achilleus said he was happy to see the faces of his dearest friends and asked Patroclus to mix drinks for everybody. He listened to Agamemnon's proposal, but the idea of selling his pride for whatever fortune offered, was repugnant to him. Besides, he couldn't stand Agamemnon, anyway. After each member of the envoy had spoken and pleaded with him to accept for the sake of the Achaians, Achilleus interrupted and said, "You could be talking to me like this till morning; but I am going to save you from wasting your time, for I will never accept anything from Agamemnon. I despise him as much as death. I wouldn't marry any of his daughters even if they were as beautiful as Aphrodite. I already have made up my mind to throw my ships into the water and sail back to Phthia, tomorrow. I was happy to see you my friends, but it would be futile for you to stay any longer". They went back with heavy heart to report to Agamemnon and the other chiefs that Achilleus had rebuffed Agamemnon's treasure; he was angrier than ever. They all stayed silent. Then Diomed said, "I didn't really expect Achilleus to accept the presents, but I also can't imagine Achilleus staying out of the battle forever. I suggest Agamemnon organize our defenses and at the right time lead a counter-attack against the Trojans."

With little persuasion Dolon gave all the information the Greeks needed.

C. Agamemnon's Spy Mission.

Agamemnon found himself in a predicament he had never known before. The Trojan army had camped for the night near the ships, and there were big fires burning both around their camp and up on the walls of Troy. The fires, actually, were Hector's idea for providing illumination to discourage a sneak attack by the Greeks, but Agamemnon was unaware of that. In fact, he was wondering what the Trojans were up to. He decided to send one of his men to try to find out. Menelaos doubted anyone would accept such a dangerous assignment, but when they asked for volunteers, Diomed stood up first; "I will go" he said, "but I would like somebody to come with me". He had hardly finished speaking when nine other brave men stood up and offered to go. Agamemnon was delighted, "Diomed son of Tydeus, man close to my heart," he said, " we are proud to have you in such a delicate mission and in fact, you can choose which of these other brave men is to accompany you. Diomed didn't take long to chose Odysseus. "Thank you son of Tydeus" Odysseus said, "We better be going because there is only one third of the night left".

Hector also had the idea of sending a spy to the Greek camp. For that he offered the gift of Achilleus' chariot, when it is captured, and Dolon, the son of a rich Herald, accepted the task. As the spies from each side were walking they fell on each other. Dolon, who was quick on his feet ran toward the Greek camp, while the Greeks ran

Nestor was amazed at the beauty of Rhesus horses.

after him and caught him. With little persuasion he gave all the information the Greeks needed: about guards, Hector's intentions, and where Trojans and allies were sleeping.

He even volunteered information about Rhesus, king of Thracians, ally of Troy, who was visiting , and had made camp all the way to the left, till morning, when he was to enter Troy. He added that Rhesus was famous for his white horses, which always won first price. He asked to be taken prisoner to the ships from where his father could ransom him. But Odysseus thought otherwise. "Traitors" Odysseus said, "are disliked not only by their own people, but also by their enemies." Diomed obliged, and killed Dolon. Odysseus struck Dolon's spear into the ground to hang on it Dolon's ferret skin cap, wolf skin and bow, while praying to Athena, "We offer these to you, in preference of all the gods, please help us get those beautiful horses of

Rhesus." They rushed, because there wasn't much time left, before daybreak. They found the Thracians real fast and saw everyone was asleep, except two guards, whom they easily eliminated. By the time the sleeping men had a chance to wake up and understand what was going on, ten more Thracians lost their life, including King Rhesus. Odysseus released the king's horses and lead them away. Athena warned Diomed to rush and get away before another god wakes up the Trojans. He joined Odysseus, they mounted the horses and galloped to their camp. Nestor was amazed with the beauty of the horses.

D. Hector's Big Drive, Many Greek Chiefs Are Wounded.

The morning came fast for another day of fierce fighting. The Achaians were on and behind their wall. Zeus didn't want a stalemate he wanted the Achaians to go out to battle so that Hector could clobber them. He sent the Goddess of discord, Eris, to the Greek camp. Goddess Eris was rejoicing, and she flew over the Greek ships holding a lighted torch in each hand. She stood half way near Odysseus ship and called for the Greeks to counterattack. Agamemnon shouted to his chiefs to get their people together for battle; this time, he decided to fight in the front of the line, to make a good example of himself. His servants brought him his greaves, the armor to cover his legs below the knees and his ankle clasps, made out of silver and were used to protect the lower part of his legs. He put them on and followed with his corslet and his cuirass, his breast plate, decorated with dozens of gold and tin bosses, to protect his body. Over his shoulders he threw the golden chain from his silver scabbard, which carried his golden studded sword. He put on his helmet made out of four layers of bronze ending at the top in four impressive horsehair plumes. Then, he picked up his shield, which was made of leather supported by ten bronze circles and having twenty tin bosses all around; while, in between, a Gorgon's head was painted in blue, to terrify the enemy looking at the shield. The handle of the shield was made out of shining silver. Finally he picked his two spears with sharp bronze tips and he was ready for battle.

Eris' call had inspired Agamemnon with confidence and reinforced his belief that in order to encourage his men, he had to fight in front of the others. Agamemnon was very well aware of the risks, but he was determined. "Let us send these dogs back to their city" he cried, and pushed forward into the Trojan line. The Trojan soldiers were overwhelmed by Agamemnon's drive and dazzling armor, so they backed away, and he ended up fighting with the local leaders. Ten chieftains, including two sons of Priam, Isus and Antiphus, were killed by Agamemnon and the line in front of him retreated in disarray. Agamemnon was confident he would be chasing the Trojans and their allies all the way to their city wall.

But Zeus was disturbed by the new turn of events and back to Mount Ida he went. From there he sent Iris to tell Hector to counter attack as soon as Agamemnon was wounded. Soon after, Agamemnon threw a spear at Iphidamas, son of Antenor, and he missed. Iphidamas retaliated by throwing his spear at Agamemnon. It hit at his belt, just below his cuirass without wounding him. Agamemnon pulled his sword and killed Iphidamas. As soon as Antenor's older son Coon saw his brother dead, he sneaked on Agamemnon's side and threw a spear at him that went through Agamemnon's arm. Under excruciating pain, Agamemnon chased after Coon caught him and killed him.

Eris rejoiced, as she flew over the Greek ships holding shield torches.

Then, Eilithuiae, the goddess that sends pain to mothers at childbirth, kept sending Agamemnon more and more pain until he could hardly stand on his chariot. Reluctantly, he asked his charioteer to drive him back to the ships.

Hector, who was watching Agamemnon very carefully, knew his turn had come. Trojans, "Lycians and Dardanians," he shouted, "the high king is gone, and Zeus has promised me victory." He saw Diomed and Odysseus killing and chasing the Trojans and turned his chariot towards them. But they also were watching him and as he approached Diomed hurled his spear, which hit Hector on his helmet. He became disoriented and fell on the ground, he shook his head and bounced right up. "Dog, you got away again", Diomed shouted, "but sooner or later I will get you". In the excitement Paris got the opportunity to aim an arrow, which went through Diomed's right foot pinning him to the ground. Paris was jubilant, "my arrow didn't go to waste, I wished it had gone through your heart for the Trojans to be rid of the devil." he shouted at Diomed. "Why don't you go seduce a woman, because you are wasting your time pretending to be a fighter. Your arrow just scratched my foot, but even a boy or a girl could have done that." Diomed yelled back. But Odysseus knew Diomed was in pain; he came over and stood over him, protecting him while Diomed broke the arrow and pulled it out. As the pain was getting sharper Diomed decided to turn his chariot around and go to the ships. Odysseus was left alone, while the Trojans were advancing towards him. Brothers Socus, who recognized him, saw the opportunity for glory and they both came at him. "Famous Odysseus," the older brother yelled, as he was hurling a spear toward him, "today you have the opportunity of killing both sons of Hippasus, or my spear will send you to hell." The spear went through his shield, his cuirass and tore open his rib side. Odysseus knew, if Palace Athena had not diverted the spear, he would have been dead. Socus ran away, but before he could get too far Odysseus threw his spear, which struck his back and he fell down dead. Odysseus then pulled the spear out from his side and blood welled out. The Trojans who were watching but afraid to challenge him till then, were now encouraged and started closing a circle around him. Odysseus yelled for help. Menelaos heard him, turned and saw the situation Odysseus was in, and hailed

Mantis said the snake was a bad omen from Zeus.

huge Ajax. They both ran to help him. The Trojans ran away when they saw Ajax. Menelaos and Ajax helped Odysseus to his chariot, where he insisted he could manage to return to the ships alone.

In the mean time, Hector was attacking Nestor's and Idomeneus' groups, who were resisting his attack, when Paris drove a barbed arrow into Machaon,s shoulder. The best doctor of the Achaians could no longer take care of the wounded. To save the doctor, Nestor helped him reach his chariot and then he lashed the horses to run toward the ships. Hector's attention was then turned to Ajax who was chasing Trojan fighters. As soon as Hector approached, Zeus filled Ajax with fear and he started running with his shield over his rear to stop the arrows that were raining on him. With most of the leaders lost from the front, nobody was left to stop Hector's advance.

Achilleus, sitting out- side his tent, saw Nestor bring back a wounded man but he wasn't sure who he was, and sent Patroclus to find out. Fair Hecamede, Nestor's servant, was already busy preparing a refreshment for the exhausted men. She was mixing wine with grated goat cheese, onion juice, honey and a handful of barley meal, a combination that was both refreshing and nutritious. When Patroclus appeared at the door, Nestor took by the hand and invited him in to sit with them. Patroclus refused, "Noble sir," he said, "I can't come in, Achilleus sent me to find out who the wounded man is, and I must go back to report to him, for you know how impatient Achilleus is."

"How come Achilleus is all of a sudden concerned about what is happening to the Achaians?", Nestor asked. "Would he care that Agamemnon, Diomed and Odysseus, the most valiant chieftains of the Achaians, lie wounded in their tents; that even doctor Machaon, I just brought here is wounded; that there is nobody out there to stop Hector from burning our ships? Right now our only hope is for you to talk to Achilleus to defend us before it is too late. If you are unable to persuade him, maybe he will agree to lend you his armor so you can appear fighting on the battleground to scare the Trojans away. Patroclus was greatly moved by Nestor's words and left without answering. Outside the noise of battle was getting louder by the minute, as the Trojans were pushing the Greeks nearer their camp. When they reached the trench that was dug around the wall the Trojans stopped; they reasoned it would be risky to drive the chariots in the lower level from where it would be difficult to escape, if it became necessary. Hector ordered soldiers on chariots to dismount and continue the attack on foot as soon as the rest of the army caught up with the chariots. The Greeks had a few minutes to enter the wall through the big gates. When, Hector finally had organized the attack, an eagle flew over them clutching a red snake, which was alive and when it reached to bite the bird's chest it was let free and fell on the left side of the Trojan line.

The old man Mantis interpreted this event as a bad omen from Zeus, but Hector did not believe him and gave the order to continue the attack, with the primary goal of breaking through the large doors on the wall. A rain of stones came down from the top of the wall, which the Trojans withstood by covering their heads with their shields. The Ajaxes kept running from tower to tower to urge the Greeks to resist, but they were unable to stop the determination that Zeus had inspired in Hector. He lifted a boulder larger that two men could even move and ran with it toward the gate as fast as he could, then he let it fly at the center of the gate. Two cross bars that gave strength to the door were smashed and the hinges were pulled out. All that was left of the door were broken pieces. Hector then, called his soldiers to follow while the Greeks ran in terror to their ships.

Poseidon suspected his brother Zeus was out to commit mischief. He got on his carriage pulled by four horses, and came out of the sea, near a mountain in Samothrace from where he could see mount Ida and the Greek encampment. He tied the horses and fed them ambrosial oats, then he entered the Greek camp disguised

Poseidon the earthshaker, got on his carriage pulled by four horses and went to boost the Greek moral.

as augur Calchas. He approached the Ajaxes, the only ones left to provide reasonable resistance to Hector, to appraise them of the situation and to instill in them the courage to fight. With a voice of ten thousand men he shouted, "Achaians shame on you, you behave like young children. You must fight if you want to save your ships." The Greeks were encouraged and fierce fighting ensued between Trojans and the Greeks, who understood it was important to defend the towers.

When the noise of the battle nearby got very loud, Nestor left wounded Machaon in his tent and went looking for Agamemnon and the other leaders for decisions. He soon spotted Agamemnon, Diomed and Odysseus walking with difficulty because of their injuries, and looking to see what was happening. "I see the Achaians running in every direction, they don't even know what danger they are running from," said

Nestor. "I don't blame them running for their lives," said Agamemnon. Odysseus was astonished at Agamemnon's callousness. "Is that what you have to say, instead of giving orders to save the ships?" said Odysseus. Before Agamemnon was given a chance to answer, Poseidon, disguised himself as an old man standing by, also had a question, "My king, I think Achilleus is selfishly watching his comrades being slaughtered, but pretty soon he will have to worry about his own life, do you think I am right? Agamemnon did not answer, he was overwhelmed.

Hera entices Zeus up on Mount Ida.

E. Hera's intrigue.

Hera looked down from her golden throne on top of Mt. Olympus and was delighted to see her brother Pocei supporting the Greeks at their encampment. But her pleasure was immediately offset by the image of her husband sitting at the top of mount Ida. How, she thought, do women put up with those husbands all over the world? And that question gave her an idea. Women control their husbands by seducing them; it would just require a little work; while always a beautiful woman she hadn't done this for a long time. She went into her secret dressing room, Hephaestus had made for her, where she washed her skin with ambrosial lotion to remove all stains from her skin, and used a drop of that ambrosial perfume that made the earth and heaven smell like spring flowers, the one she knew Zeus couldn't resist. Then she tricked Aphrodite to lend her the art of seduction, stored in a magic girdle, pretending she needed it for an aunt and uncle. Now she was ready; but before flying to Zeus she stopped at Lemnos to find "Ypnos" (pronounced epnos), the god of sleep, brother of Death. "My dear Ypnos", she said, "lord of both mortals and immortals when they lay down to rest, I need a favor from you. Give sweet rest to the eyes of Zeus after I find him on top of the Mt. Ida." Ypnos was worried, "Oh no, your highness," he said, "tell me to put anyone to sleep and I can help you; but All Mighty Zeus, without him ordering me, I can't. I remember what happened the last time, when you wanted to release that hurricane against Hercules; when the all mighty woke up he was chasing me like a wild animal, and it was a good thing Night protected me, otherwise it would have been the end of me."

Hera told him to relax; that at that time Zeus was angry, but now he is going to be in a good mood because I will be with him." "O.K." Ypnos said, "I will do it if you promise me you are going to fix it between me and the beautiful Favor Pasithea." Hera agreed, now she was ready.

She flew by Mt. Ida opening her dress for some of that perfume to spread all over Asia. As soon as Zeus smelled the perfume he knew Hera was in view. " Where do you think you are going", he asked. "I am going to visit our relatives from our mother's side, who are having marital difficulties, and I thought I would pass by here and say hello to you.", she answered. "That is not the way wives say hello to their husbands", he said and pulled her next to him. "You have plenty of time for your visit, later. Now I would love to be together with you for awhile." "I am bashful", she said, "every god can see us sleep together, here at the top of the mountain." Zeus, to please her, ordered a golden cloud to cover the whole of Mount Ida. A little while later, Ypnos came to sweetly close his eye lids, and Zeus was fast asleep. Hera immediately sent Ypnos to notify Poseidon of what she had done. Poseidon saw the opportunity, he pulled his long, sharp sword and shouted at the Achaians to follow him as he was attacking the Trojans. The Greeks were ready to follow a leader. Even Agamemnon, Diomed and Odysseus, despite their wounds, armed themselves and joined the fight. Hector threw his spear at Ajax, but the protective cuirass on his chest saved him from a wound; Ajax, in turn threw a boulder at Hector's chest. Hector spun around and fell, with blood coming out of his mouth, but he was saved as some of his brave fighters and allies, rushed to pull him away.

When Zeus woke up in Hera's embrace, he took a look at the Greek camp and saw Poseidon ahead of the Achaians chasing the Trojans back where they had left their chariots. Hector was seriously wounded, vomiting blood, and the Trojan moral was at its lowest. Zeus immediately understood Hera's game and he became enraged. "Treacherous woman", he shouted, "you don't give up, but your crooked mind invents evil tricks to prevail. Only, I doubt you will now find a way to escape the trouble you are in. How would you like going back hanging from a cloud, which I can make special for you? I can make it beautifully golden in color with gold chains and anvils to match, tying both your wrists and ankles together for eternity; or maybe I should whip you until your body becomes black and blue. And that Ypnos, wait till I get my hands on him." "You don't have to get angry at me because your brother, who is old enough to use his own brain, felt sorry and tried to save the Achaians from total destruction at your hands; I swear to the waters of the river Styx and our bridal bed that whatever Poseidon did has nothing to do with me. Now feel happy that you have me in tears", she said. And Zeus smiled at her and said, "don't worry I will find out how much of what you say is true. In the mean time get ready to join the rest of them on top of Mt. Olympus. And tell Iris and Apollo that I want to see them.

Zeus was glad Iris and Apollo showed up, though Hera hadn't even left yet. He gave Apollo the task of doctoring Hector and to send back to fight. He sent Iris to tell Poseidon to stop fighting for the Greeks and go home. Then, alone with Hera, he described to her his plan, how he intended to end the Trojan war with the destruction of Troy and the role Patroclus, Achilleus and Hector would have to play in it. None of the other gods or goddesses would be allowed to intervene. Hera didn't answer, she left instantly and returned to Mt. Olympus where she received a hero's reception. Back in the Greek camp, Iris informs Poseidon of Zeus will, he would either obey or be punished. Poseidon was greatly insulted, "We were three brothers" he said, "Zeus got the heaven, I got the sea, and Pluto got the underworld. Zeus may be overestimating his strength." "Do you want me to give that

Night protects Ypnos from Zeus' rage.

answer to Zeus?" Iris asked. "There will be no answer until I see the results of his plan of action, " Poseidon said, and plunged into the waters of the Aegean Sea.

Hector, who thought he was dying, found himself in perfect health with a stranger besides him telling him of Zeus' order to get his men together and counter-attack.

He was assured, the Achaians would run like jack rabbits. He realized a God was talking to him, and, yes, he did mention Phoebus. Hector felt a weight had been lifted from his chest, and the image of Hades disappeared from his thoughts. He proudly raised his head to see a crowd of ecstatic people about him.

The Trojans knew Zeus was with them; while, to the Achaians, Hector had escaped Hades and was coming to punish them. They decided there was no use standing and fighting against gods' will; so they ran, leaving the bravest men behind them. Before long the Trojans were again inside the trench in front of the Greek wall. As

The Trojans holding torches reached the Greek ships

they were deciding how to overcome this obstacle, Apollo pushed the center section of the wall down, they only had to walk through. "Trojans, Lycians and Dardanians," Hector shouted, go burn their ships and I will finish the Greeks who are still running behind. Zeus made Ajax' hands feel tired from fighting and the only thing he could do was shout at the others to defend themselves. At this point each of the Greeks was asking to be saved by his fellow man. The Trojans gathered in front of Protesilaos' boat with torches, ready to burn it.

VII. PATROCLUS IS KILLED WHILE IMPERSONATING ACHILLEUS IN THE BATTLEFIELD.

Patroclus on his way back to Achilleus, stopped to help a fighter named Eurypylus, who was wounded by an arrow in his thigh; but before he could spend much time with the man the noise of the battle from the ships alarmed him. He turned the care of the man to his charioteer, and ran to Achilleus in tears. Achilleus asked him if he had heard any bad news about their families in Greece, and Patroclus informed him of most of the leaders, including the high king being wounded and the Trojans in the Greek camp ready to start burning the ships. Then he asked Achilleus, if there was an oracle that prevented him from fighting, why couldn't he borrow his armor to lead the Myrmidons and save the fleet. Achilleus' answer was, "I will lend you my armor with the understanding that as soon as Hector retreats from the camp, you will return here." Patroclus promised, and ran to put on Achilleus armor. Now they could see the flames and smoke from two ships that were set on fire by Hector. There was no time to lose. Achilleus' army, some twenty five hundred Myrmidons, were assembled and Achilleus' divine team of horses were yoked, and teamed with an additional fast horse, for Patroclus' chariot. Achilleus spoke to his soldiers who were lined so close to each other, their shields formed a continuous wall. "You have been complaining I was keeping you out of the battle. Well, you win. You are now entrusted with the high duty of chasing the Trojans out of the Greek camp and save our ships. I am sure you will honor Phthia." They all voiced enthusiasm. Achilleus, after first washing his hands, brought out the special glass he used only for prayer, he filled, it with water and wine, and poured Zeus a toast. He looked up toward the sky and prayed to Zeus for his army to be victorious in the imminent battle and for Patroclus safe return. Zeus heard the words but he was ready to grant only the first part of the prayer.

When the Trojans saw the Myrmidons lead by that unmistakable armor of Achilleus on his well known chariot, it was like seeing a destructive ghost from the past which they wanted nothing to do with. First they ran over the easiest ground which was the coast, before turning toward the Trojan plain. Patroclus went after their leaders, usually on chariots killing whomever he could catch up with, for there was no attempt by anyone turning to resist. When the Achaian leaders saw what was happening, they were quick to join in the fight. Patroclus was thus unopposed, until he caught up with Sarpedon, king of Lycians, son of Zeus and a mortal. He jumped down from his chariot, indicating he was ready to face Patroclus in single combat. Patroclus, also descended from his chariot. Two brave fighters were now facing each other and Hades was ready for at least one of them. Zeus not only could see what was happening, but he also knew his son's Fate was death. "I think I am going to defy the Fates, pick him up from the battleground and bring him safely to his land, he murmured. But that was loud enough for Hera to hear and she was known to be very unsympathetic to the illegitimate children of her husband. "No, you won't she said; I mean I don't think you should," she corrected. "There are many gods and goddesses that have their darling children fighting, and your doing what you are thinking will upset the order of Fates." Zeus agreed and Sarpedon's fate was thus sealed, his spear missed Patroclus, who then threw his spear through Sarpedon's heart. This was a big blow to the Trojans, because Sarpedon, was their bravest and trusted ally. Achaians and Trojans fought hard to gain access to Sarpedon's body. Zeus, in his grief, asked

Zeus, in his grief, ordered Apollo to take Sarpedon's body away.

Phoebus Apollo to take Sarpedon away from the battleground, for the body to be thoroughly washed and anointed with ambrosia; "Then, let the gods sleep and his brother Death carry the body to his country and his royal family and friends for a hero's burial, under a mount and a pillar", Zeus concluded.

When the Trojans saw Sarpedon's body disappear, they were panic stricken and ran toward the city with Patroclus' army in pursuit. But when Hector arrived at the gates of Troy, Apollo inspired him to turn his chariot around and come back to fight Patroclus. Apollo, disguised as a dark mist, went behind Patroclus and gave him a karate blow behind his neck, causing Patroclus' helmet to fly away and roll on the ground. Simultaneously, Apollo had his shield slip off his shoulder and his corselet unbuttoned. Patroclus, understood his end was near, he stood there confused and powerless. A Dardanian came around and speared his back. Patroclus tried to withdraw, but Hector came at him and speared him in the naval area. Patroclus was doomed and Hector was jubilant. "Here is Patroclus who was going to enslave our women, but now he is destined for the dogs and the vultures", he teased. Patroclus' last words were, "Zeus and Phoebus gave you victory, but don't rejoice; by killing me you wrote your destiny. You are going to die by the hand of my friend Achilleus, who is going to avenge me." "Who knows", said Hector, "maybe he will also die by my hand."

Despite the effort by the Myrmidons, to secure Patroclus' body, Hector was able to strip Achilleus' armor and send it to his house in Troy. Achilleus' Olympian horses Xanthus and Balius ran away and went and stood by the river crying. Zeus felt sorry for them. "We shouldn't be giving Olympian horses to mortals" he thought. He sent courage to Automedon, the charioteer, who took the chariot through a wide curve, practically running over a few Trojan fighters, back to camp. The fighting around the body continued. Menelaos ran to the scene as soon as he heard Patroclus was dead and called Ajax for help. Zeus felt sorry for the Greeks and sent Athena, who helped them take hold of Patroclus body, but Hector kept attacking so that the final outcome was not in view.

Achilleus was standing in front of his tent when he saw a cloud of dust in the battlefield, approaching. He immediately understood there was trouble, and he imagined the worse, that Patroclus was dead. His mother foretold him that before his end, the Myrmidons would lose one of their best. Then Antilochus, son of Nestor ran to him and confirmed, that Patroclus was killed and they were still struggling around his body. Achilleus became hysterical; he took a handful of black ashes and threw them over his head, then rubbed his hands over his face, while he fell down hitting the ground with his fists. The slave girls ran around him with compassion. Achilleus, who didn't want to be seen crying by women, got up and ran to the sea shore.

Thetis heard her son screaming, from the bottom of the ocean and ran to console him. "Do you want to tell me what aches you, my son?" she asked. He told her Hector, not only killed Patroclus, but he also striped the armor out of his body. "Now", Achilleus said, "I must avenge his death by killing Hector and many Trojans, in his honor; but Hector has my armor, and non other fits me except Huge Ajax's, who also needs it to fight." "Don't worry my son", Thetis said, I will have Hephaestus make you the best armor in the world, and I will bring it to you here by tomorrow morning. Till then, stay out of battle as I don't want you to get hurt!" Thetis left. She first went back to her cavern at the bottom of the ocean, where she asked her sister Nereids to lament for Patroclus. They started singing and hitting their naked bodies with their hands. Then she flew to Lemnos to find Hephaestus, who welcomed Thetis' visit, for it was her, who had kept him at her house for nine years to recuperate, when Hera didn't like the way his legs looked and tossed him to the bottom of Olympus.

When he heard her request for a new armor for Achilleus, Hephaestus felt happy he could be of help and went right to work.

Meanwhile Hera was observing the struggle around Patroclus body. She wanted to make sure the Trojans could not win by taking it. She sent Iris to persuade Achilleus to go help chase the Trojans away. "How can you sit here while brave men fight to save the integrity of the body of your friend? what will people say if you allow your friend to arrive in Hades without a head or arms?" Achilleus temper started boiling; despite his mothers instructions, not to enter any conflict till she brought him a new

Thetis hears her son and, comes from the bottom of the sea to console him.

armor, he stood out and shouted at the Trojans, challenging them. Athena strengthened his voice and added a thousand echoes. The Trojans were terrified to see and hear Achilleus threatening them and they ran in panic. Thus, finally, Patroclus' body was brought home.

Hera felt relieved and realized she could now order the sun god Helios to plunge in the ocean to the West. As darkness came, the Trojans called for a council of the leaders to decide whether they should stay in their temporary camp, not too far from the Greek ships, or retreat to the safety of the City walls, as wise Polydamas was suggesting. Hector didn't want to hear about retreat. "If Achilleus tries to attack us I will have the chance to finish him too", Hector boasted. The council liked his bravado attitude and voted to stay in their present camp.

VIII. ACHILLEUS, DEVASTATED BY PATROCLUS DEATH, GOES FOR REVENGE.

Achilleus gave orders for preparations. He commanded a big cauldron on tripods to be set over a fire to warm water that would be needed to wash Patroclus body. The night would allow time for the Achaians to mourn for Patroclus' loss. Achilleus was in agony. He was thinking of the time he had promised Patroclus' father that he was going to protect and bring his son back safe and glorious, with treasures captured from the sacking of Troy. "Not only did he not make an effort to keep Patroclus from

The Nereids lamenting, they sang and hit their naked bodies with their hands.

going and fight alone", he thought, "but he encouraged him by lending him his armor, while he himself stayed back out of danger. That was not due to that oracle about his end being near", he thought, "but what will people think?" All the glory he has worked so hard to build will now be gone, if people think of him as a coward." Now, he will have to go back to fight Hector, in spite of his word to the Achaians he would never fight under Agamemnon's command. He went and sat next to Patroclus, whose body was by now washed and dressed. "My dear friend, it will not be long before I will join you, allow me to delay your funeral until I can avenge you by bringing Hector's body next to your Pyre, and killing a dozen prisoners. Till then, please stay with us, we will have all the captured women mourn over you day and night".

Back in Lemnos, Hephaestus was working hard with copper, tin , silver and gold to make Achilleus' armor, he had promised Thetis. To make the shield, he used five layers of metals, the strong ones like tin and hardened copper inside, and gold and silver outside. On the outside the shield showed the earth and the sky with the sun and the moon, the Pleiades, Orion and the Dippers with Polaris, the only star that does not move as time goes and never dips into the ocean. He also illustrated village scenes; in one scene, a bride is escorted by friends and relatives to her new home with the young people dancing to the sounds of the flute and the lyre. When the shield was finished, Hephaestus labored over a breastplate out of shiny metals,

Achilleus sat next to Patroclus body; "My friend, I will soon join you", he said.

brighter than fire, like gold and silver. Finally, the helmet he made out of bronze and dipped its entire edge in molten gold, so that when the sun was shining up high, the eyes of the enemy would be dazed by its brilliance. Thetis, who was waiting, was dazzled when Hephaestus laid all the pieces in front of her. "It is all yours", he said, and she was pleased and grateful. She then picked up the armor and flew to the Greek camp. Achilleus was still laying next to Patroclus' body with a crowd of slave women and Myrmidon fighters all around.

"My son, take a few minutes away from Patroclus to see what I have brought you," she said. They both moved at the end of the tent, where Thetis showed Achilleus the new Armor. "Mother", he said, "it is worthy of its maker, it is beautiful." Before she left, Thetis poured ambrosia on Patroclus wounds to keep the flesh intact.

Achilleus was anxious to arrange things for rejoining the battle. He called a general meeting at the seashore, where he reconciled with Agamemnon; he not only put Achilleus in charge of the next attack, but also instructed Odysseus to pickup all he had previously offered to Achilleus, from Agamemnon's quarters, including Briseis and the seven slave women and deliver to Achilleus' tent. Shortly after, Agamemnon, Odysseus, Menelaos and Diomed, walking with difficulty and using their spears for support because of their wounds, arrived at Achilleus tent to pay respect to Patroclus. Achilleus was crying hysterically, and soon they couldn't help but join in the weeping.

Athena helped dawn arrive and find Achilleus exhausted and hungry, as he had refused any food, even water, since he had learned of Patroclus death. Athena was concerned of letting him go to battle in this condition; so she flew by and dropped onto his body an ethereal mixture of nectar and ambrosia to sustain him for the day. Now all the Greeks started getting ready for battle. They were arming themselves and ran, like snow flakes to their assigned positions. Achilleus put on his new armor, which was as bright as the full moon. His Olympian horses were yoked and Automedon, his charioteer, brought the chariot to him. "I hope this time you behave better", Achilleus said to the horses, "In case anything happens to me, don't go cry by the river, but bring me home." Xanthus, who was endowed by Hera to speak, answered, "We are not responsible for Patroclus body having been seized, for it was Phoebus

Thetis brings new armor by Hephaestus to her son.

Apollo that caused Patroclus death, Hector only gave the final blow. The same way, our lord, you are destined to die in the hands of both a mortal and an immortal." "Those are bad manners Xanthus to prophesy the death of your master." Achilleus remarked.

Zeus was finally satisfied that things were going well and according to plan. He felt bad about his recent authoritative behavior over the other gods, and decided to allow them more freedom. He assigned, goddess Themis the task of calling all gods to a general council. And he emphasized that by "All gods" he meant every god, goddess, Nymph and even river gods. Poseidon, still wet with sea water, asked Zeus what the purpose of the meeting was. Zeus answered that while he intends to sit on his throne and watch the war, he wanted everybody to know that he was freeing them to participate in the war in any way they please. Gods on the same side moved close whispering to each other. One could tell which gods favored which side. Hermes and Hephaestus moved next to Hera, Athena and Poseidon, on the Greeks' side. The gathering around Apollo, including his sister Artemis and their mother Leto (mistress of Zeus), Ares, Aphrodite, and the god of River Scamander who was obviously pro-Trojan.

As soon as Zeus allowed them, the gods rushed to the front.

"I see each side is well represented" Zeus started saying, but before he had quite finished, the two groups had disappeared. They were already in the battlefield.

Apollo convinced Aeneas that, as son of Aphrodite, he had a better chance of defeating Achilleus, who was the son of Thetis, a minor goddess. However, when Aeneas challenged Achilleus, Poseidon covered Achilleus eyes with a dark mist, then pulled Aeneas out of the fight and flew him to the end of the line. "It was foolish of you to compete with Achilleus. Next time you try that, Hades will surely have you", Poseidon said. When Achilleus eyes finally cleared, Aeneas was gone. "I recognize a miracle when I see one", he said, and went back to search for Hector. Poseidon, anxious to do something used what he could do best, shake the earth. The fighters stopped fighting and struggled to stay on their feet. Pluto, the god of the underworld, became very concerned that if the dome of Hades were to crack and fall the

sun could shine on the dead, which would be a catastrophe. The Trojans were particularly terrified because they knew Poseidon was against them, so they fled. Most ran to the plain, toward Troy, the others decided to seek protection in the River, for they knew the god of the Scamander River, also known as Xanthus, was on their side.
 Achilleus sent his soldiers to chase the Trojans on the plain, while he jumped into the river killing anyone that raised his head out of the water to breath. Xanthus rose from the waters as Achilleus was tossing a dead Trojan to his lap. "You can cause just as much destruction on land, instead of polluting and coloring my water red with

Xanthus rose from the waters as Achilleus tossed a dead Trojan on his laps.

blood" the river god said. Xanthus then started raising tall waves against Achilleus, who immediately found out that his shield could not protect him from the waves and the river currents. His heavy armor was pushing him under, and he started calling the gods for help. Poseidon and Athena ran to his rescue disguised as peasants.
They told him Poseidon and Athena sent them because it was not his fate to drown in the river. Xanthus persisted and sent his waves further outside his banks, flooding the plain. Hera got concerned. She called her son Hephaestus to the rescue. The crooked foot god, obliged with a ball of fire that rolled over the dead Trojans on the land and reached Scamander's banks charring the beautiful elms, willows, and tamarisks. Even the fish and the eels, gasped for air. Xanthus prayed to Hera for her son to stop the blaze, and said he surrenders; he will never act on behalf of Troy,

again. Hera heard Xanthus and called Hephaestus, "That is enough my crooked foot" she yelled, and her son obeyed his mother and extinguished the fire.

Zeus from his throne had a great time watching the battle field, where the fight between mortals, was now turning into a quarrel between members of his own family. Ares saw Athena in the middle of the battle and felt Zeus presented him with an opportunity. "Bitch" he shouted, "you are going to pay for all your mischief against me," as he was pushing his spear against her tasseled shield, but she withdrew in time. She picked a rugged black stone and hurled it at Ares, hitting him at the neck. His Ichor started bubbling out of the wound as he lost consciousness and fell into the dust. "Dummy, when are you going to learn that you are no match for me" Athena shouted laughingly. Aphrodite helped Ares get up; they would have walked away if Hera had not alerted Athena, who slapped Aphrodite's breast and both Ares and Aphrodite found themselves stretched on the ground.

Poseidon challenged Apollo to a duel, but Apollo said it wasn't worth fighting for the sake of mortals, who perish like autumn leaves. Artemis then teased Apollo that he only carries the bow and arrows for show. Hera heard that and got furious; she picked Artemis by the wrists using her left hand, while with the right hand she took her bow to whip her ears. Artemis' arrows were spilled all over the Ground and Artemis was screaming. Her mother Leto ran and helped Artemis gather her bow and arrows. Hera said to Leto, "I won't fight you, as I don't want to give anybody the opportunity to gossip about Zeus' wives fighting.

IX. HECTOR'S BITTER END.

That day was not a good day for the Trojans. Priam watched from high up on the wall, half his army being chased all the way to the walls of Troy. "Open all the gates for our fighters to enter", he shouted. " When the last soldier and ally is safe, lock the doors and defend the City." For the Trojans and their allied fighters Ilion was like a harbor where the boat can find shelter from the stormy sea. They came sweating, hungry and thirsty and found relief before they positioned themselves on top of the wall ready to defend the City. Hector, had given the order for his army to retreat when he saw the tremendous losses they were suffering under the Achaian's advance, lead by Achilleus wrath; but when he reached the Scaean Gate, he did not enter. He remembered his boasting during the council meeting the night before, that he would be happy to face Achilleus. Now, he thought, "Look at the losses in human life we suffered because I did not listen to Polydamas' advice to retreat. Well, it is too late to change things now for he already could see Achilleus' shiny armor galloping towards him. He knew the odds, but he had to stand and face the consequences. He looked up toward the city at the top of the wall, perhaps for the last time. His father, Priam, was standing there trying to talk to him by gesturing with his hands. He understood he was begging him to enter the gate; but he disregarded his plea. Then his mother Hecuba ran next to his father was also pleading with him to enter the gate. Instead of complying, he placed his heavy shield next to the wall, awaiting Achilleus. His mother understood he was not yielding to their pleas. As a last resort, Hecuba tore her blouse to show Hector the breast that suckled him as a baby. But nothing worked. He knew Polydamas, would blame him for his stupid decision to remain on the plain, instead of retreating. Achilleus, who looked like the god of war, approached and jumped from his chariot holding his well known long spear. Hector panicked and started running along the walls with Achilleus in hot pursuit. Apollo strengthened Hector's lungs and legs so Achilleus, the fastest runner known, could not catch him. Hector's plan was to run close to the wall, especially near the Dardanian gates where Trojan fighters could kill Achilleus with arrows and spears. Achilleus kept cutting him off, keeping him away from the wall. While they were Greek fighters around, Achilleus signaled for all to stay out of the fight — he wanted to fight Hector alone. All the gods were watching. Zeus, who liked Hector, was tempted to save him, but Athena wouldn't hear of such a thing. "Father," she said, we can't change anybody's fate, you are in charge, but don't expect us to agree." Zeus took out his balance, assigning one tray to Achilleus, the other to Hector and held it; the balance started horizontal, but the Fates caused Hector's tray to plunge. It was then clear to all gods, including Apollo, that Hector was doomed. Athena, was given permission by Zeus to hasten the process. She first flew to tell Achilleus to stop, to catch his breath, while she convinced Hector to stop running and turn to fight. She next appeared to Hector disguised as his brother, Deiphobus, pretending to be joining him against Achilleus. Hector was encouraged. He turned around and faced Achilleus, who hurled his long spear at him. Hector bent down, allowing the spear to fly over him. Then Hector threw his spear at Achilleus, it struck but failed to penetrate the middle of Achilleus shield with no harm to Achilleus. Hector then asked for Deiphobus' spear, but he got no response. He turned and saw his brother had disappeared. He immediately understood that Athena had played a trick on him and that the gods had decided his doom. He pulled his sword and went at Achilleus, to whom Athena had brought bach his spear. Achilleus aimed and hit Hector at a section of his neck, which was not protected by the armor he had captured from Patroclus. Hector fell, but he was able to plead with Achilleus to allow his father to ransom his body. Achilleus refused, telling him that he should have thought of that when he killed Patroclus, and now, his body was destined for the dogs and the vultures. Hector had a bitter end. Achilleus stripped Hector's body naked and after he tied Hector's legs to his chariot he dragged him around the wall of Troy. Hecuba, who was watching from the top of the wall threw away her veil while she was screaming and pulling her hair. Priam next to her, covered his eyes as he was lowering his head to the to the ground. Andromache heard the screams and rushed from her house to the top of the wall with her servant, as Achilleus started dragging Hector's body around the wall of Troy.

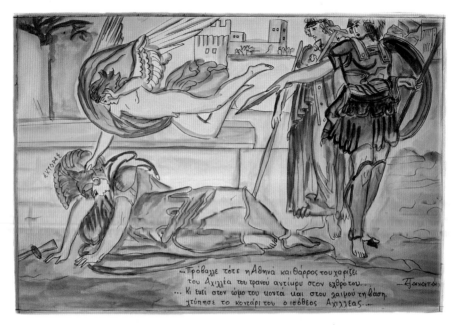

"Now your body is destined for the dogs and the vultures," Achilleus said.

Andromache heard the screams and ran to the wall with her maid.

Andromache faints as women break her fall and support her.

Achilleus tied Hector's legs to his chariot and dragged him around the wall of Troy.

X. PATROCLUS IS PUT TO REST WITH HONORS.

At the camp, Achilleus ordered his Myrmidons to honor their dead before they unharnessed the horses, by slowly dragging Hector's body three times around Patroclus bier — a wooden box without a cover to be burned later with the body. A period of lamentation followed and Achilleus lead his Myrmidon army in singing and crying. Thetis, while invisible, was responsible for an excessive shedding of tears. The men were moved when Achilleus placed his blood-stained hand on Patroclus chest saying, "Farewell, my friend, even though to the house of Hades. I, up here, will do everything I promised you." The time then came for the men to take care of the horses and gather for the funeral feast, where herds of oxen, sheep, goats, and boars were sacrificed, then cooked over charcoal for everyone to have a full portion of meat and wine.

The Greek leaders persuaded Achilleus to follow them to Agamemnon's tent, where they had warmed water for him to wash, but Achilleus refused, saying that he would not use water on his body until he places Patroclus' bier on his pyre. The visit gave Achilleus the opportunity to ask Agamemnon to send men up on mount Ida to cut wood for the Patroclus' pyre. "I will do so" Agamemnon said, if you join us now for dinner." They all found big portions to satisfy their hunger. All then went to sleep, but Achilleus sat near the sea shore, still thinking about the loss of Patroclus. Feeling tired, the sound of the waves as they rolled on the sand, helped close his eyes and Achilleus finally fell asleep. Patroclus' ghost came in his dream, fully dressed, looking as handsome as ever. He asked Achilleus to hurry up with his pyre, so that his flesh could be purified; before then the doors of Hades, he said, remain closed for him. A final request was that his ashes be saved in a jar, where the ashes of Achilleus could, before long, also be placed; thus the two friends would be buried and remain together for ever. Achilleus tried to embrace him, but Patroclus disappeared.

With all the available men in the camp assigned to gathering wood, preparations for the pyre were quickly completed. According to Achilleus' planning, the bier with Patroclus' body was to be brought to the site of the pyre by a procession, where all the chariots, with their fighters and charioteers would form a single line, followed by the thousands of fighters on foot. First, each of Patroclus friends was given the time to cut one of his curls and deposit it on Patroclus body in the bier. Then, Achilleus cut the curl he had dedicated to the River-God Spercheious, from his own head and placed it between Patroclus fingers. The bier was then lifted and taken to the pyre site in the middle of the procession, with Achilleus supporting one side. When they reached the pyre site, Achilleus asked Agamemnon to dismiss the soldiers, as it was already supper time, while the Myrmidons would take care of the burning of Patroclus' body.

As soon as the big crowd left, the Myrmidons slaughtered herds of sheep and cattle from which Achilleus took fat and covered Patroclus bier. In addition two of Patroclus nine dogs and twelve Trojan prisoners were slain. The carcasses were placed to burn along the periphery of the wood pile, while the center was reserved exclusively for Patroclus bier, lest his ashes became mixed with that of the animals. Hector's body was brought and placed next to the pyre, and Aphrodite kept the dogs away. She even sprayed ambrosial perfume over Hector's body to keep it intact. Apollo helped by covering it with a dark cloud. When everything was ready, the Myrmidons tried to set fire at several points of the woodpile, but the green wood wouldn't catch fire. Achilleus prayed and poured wine, to Boreas, god of the North wind, and Zephyr, god of the West wind, to help the hesitant flames. Goddess Iris, the messenger, heard Achilleus plea and flew to find the wind gods, who at the time were having a feast in their small island. She was invited to join, but she refused. She gave them Achilleus message and they were happy to help. Dark clouds formed along their path, and when they arrived at Patroclus Pyre they blew their hardest and the flames were raised to the sky. By then Achilleus was exhausted, and as soon as he sat by the side of the pyre he fell asleep. He was awakened in the morning by Agamemnon, who had come with his councilors. Achilleus looked at the pyre which had subsided, but still glowing red. "My lord," he said to Agamemnon, "I am going to need your help to quench the hot bones, by pouring wine on them, around the center of the pyre; I can then collect the bones and save them in a golden jar, until the time comes to add mine to them." A cloud of steam with ashes rose as goatskins full of wine were emptied on the hot cinders. Patroclus' bones were then collected and placed in the jar, according to Achilleus wishes.

As it was customary to further honor the dead after the pyre ceremony was completed, Achilleus declared competitive games: chariot and foot racing, wrestling, boxing, discus and javelin throwing. The prizes were: a slave woman and a three-legged cauldron, an unbroken mare, an unused copper cauldron, two ingots of gold, a bronze urn, a mule, a goblet, an engraved silver mixing bowl, and a fat ox. Of the thousands of soldiers who participated, the winners were the usual heros, Diomed, Ajax, Odysseus, Agamemnon, Nestor and his son Antilochus.

XI. HECTOR'S BODY IS RANSOMED BY PRIAM.

By the time the competitive games had finished it was evening, and the crowd was hungry. After dinner, every one, except those on guard duty, were happy to lie down for a good night's sleep. Achilleus, could not fall asleep. The loss of Patroclus was still on his mind. After awhile, he got up and walked along the shore, then he yoked his horses, tied Hector's body to the rear of his chariot and drove three times around Patroclus tomb, as he was crying. Apollo could not stand to see this happening to his favored Trojan and used his golden aegis to protect Hector's face from being damaged. The other gods, who also watched, with the exception of Hera, Poseidon, and the gray-eyed Athena, were equally unhappy with Achilleus' shameful behavior and tried to urge Hermes to steal Hector's body. "How can you watch this and do nothing, Apollo howled at the other gods. Didn't Hector burn thighbones of young cows and goats covered with fat for your sake? Are you going to allow Achilleus to behave like a wild lion? People grieve when they lose brothers, but they get over it; Achilleus refuses to accept the will of Fates." But Hera objected. "How can you talk like that about Achilleus, son of a Goddess Thetis, whom I raised, for the sake of Hector, who was born and breast-fed by a mortal. At this point Zeus thought it was time to intervene. "If we let Hermes steal the body, Thetis will know and tell Achilleus. It would be better if I talked to Thetis to convince Achilleus to let the body be ransomed by Hector's father Priam." Iris was immediately summoned to go fetch Thetis from her cavern at the bottom of the ocean between Samos and Imbros, where she was sitting with the other nymphs lamenting for her sons death to come. Thetis was surprised that Zeus wanted to see her, but she followed Iris and the waves parted as the two goddesses zipped through the waters; then the gates of Olympus spread wide open for them to fly in. Athena offered Thetis her seat and Hera a cup of nectar, which she drunk. Zeus then told her of his decision to ransom Hector's body to Priam and expected her to talk to Achilleus. Iris was sent to talk to Priam.

Thetis found Achilleus still crying in his tent. She sat next to him and caressed his hair. "How long are you going to keep this up, my son? You torture yourself and waste the short life that is left in you. Zeus sent me to tell you that the gods are angry and that you must give Hector's body to Priam in exchange for a rich ransom. Achilleus reasoned out that he could not disobey the gods, especially Zeus and accepted.

Iris found Priam grieving in despair. His whole body was filthy from rolling on the ground and throwing dirt all over himself. The lament of his daughters and daughters-in-law, sitting up on the roof, could be heard from all over the palace. With her sweet voice Iris explained to Priam that it was Zeus' will for him to meet with Achilleus alone, but with enough presents to soften his heart to release Hector; that Achilleus, while also grieved and angry about Patroclus death, was generous, with a good heart, and with respect for the elderly. Despite Hecuba's objections, Priam ordered his sons to yoke his horses and mules and get the wagon ready; then called Idaeus, the capable charioteer, for a driver. Priam, himself, prepared the ransom he would present to Achilleus: a dozen cloaks, vests, shirts and rugs; ten talents of gold, two shinny tripods with four cauldrons, and a precious cup. He packed everything and had three of his sons carry them to the wagon. Then he prayed to Zeus, who imme-

Iris was sent to Priam to tell him he could ransom Hector's body.

diately sent his best eagle to fly over the wagon as an omen that Priam's trip would be successful. The horses and mules were happy to be out from the stable and started running with the first signal from Idaeus. They went through the streets of Troy and soon were running out in the open plain under the night sky.

At the river, where they stopped to water the horses, Idaeus pointed out to Priam a suspicious character, standing nearby. Priam was terrified at first, but the stranger approached and with a very sweet and polite voice he teased, "Aren't you afraid, two old men like you to move valuable goods in the night? I really feel sorry for you, as you remind me of my father. Don't be afraid, I will guide and protect you from strangers and Achaian soldiers." With these words he jumped into the wagon and took over the reins of the horses and mules; he instilled into the animals new strength to quickly cover the rest of the plain to the Achaian trench. Priam felt obliged for the help from the stranger and offered him a precious chalice. Hermes refused and revealed his identity, sent by his father Zeus to help. Hermes put the guards at the gate to sleep, then pulled the huge bolt to open the gate; soon after, they reached Achilleus tent. "Sir", he said, "you reached your destination, now you will have to enter alone, for Achilleus is not supposed to see me, and I must go back to Olympus.

Priam opened the door and walked in. He immediately saw Achilleus sitting at the end of the tent. He ran and knelt in front of him, put his arms around Achilleus legs and kissed his hands. "Oh Achilleus, have pity of me, think of your father, who is old as I am. Out of my fifty sons, eighteen with Hecuba and the others with other women under my roof, Hector was my best, the defender of our city, slain by your hands. For the fear of gods please accept my valuable presents as a ransom for his body." Achilleus was deeply moved; he took Priam gently by the hand to help him get up and offered him a seat nearby. "I pity you and admire your courage to come here alone, to kiss the hands that killed your son. My mother has told me that in Zeus' palace there are two urns, where Zeus keeps his presents, pleasant presents in one, painful in the other. Before he hands them to mortals he includes some of each kind, some of them bring us happiness, the others tears. As for Hector's body, we both know, that it is god's will you return with it, so consider it ransomed, according to your wishes." With these words, Achilleus left the room, and gave orders to his servants to clean and anoint Hectors body. Then, he with his two squires unloaded the ransom and gave one of the outfits to dress Hectors body. Achilleus then lifted the body, himself, placed it into a bier and took it to Priam's wagon; there, he asked Idaeus, who was still waiting in the wagon to join Priam inside his tent. Achilleus then slaughtered a sheep and the servants prepared food for everybody. He asked Priam how many days the Trojans would need for Hector's funeral celebration, and Priam answered twelve, to which Achilleus agreed.

Priam thanked him and mentioned that as he had not slept since the day Hector was killed, he would appreciate the opportunity to get some sleep. He was lead to a couch nicely prepared with woolen blankets, where he was soon fast asleep. But Hermes could not fall asleep; as he kept thinking of how to get Priam's wagon through the Greek camp in the morning, without incidents. He decided to get moving right away. He hovered over Priam and whispered to him, "Have you thought what will happen if Agamemnon catches you in the camp tomorrow? The old man jumped up; he realized it was foolish of him to be sleeping, instead of using the night to escape. He woke up Idaeus, and both tiptoed to the wagon, which they found ready since Hermes had already yoked horses and mules and was waiting for them, holding the reins. Priam and Idaeus, climbed on to the wagon and Hermes made sure that none of the guards would notice them as he drove through the camp. As soon as they reached the river Xanthus, he handed the reins to Idaeus, and disappeared.

Soon, they were at the gate of Troy, which the guards opened. Down, in her saffron robe was shedding the veils of the night, but the city was still asleep. Only Cassandra, as beautiful as Aphrodite, was awake and waiting for them. When she saw them she started crying loudly and calling, "Men and women of Troy, you rejoiced every time Hector returned from battle, now come see him return for the last time, dead." The Trojans came crying, with desperation clear on their faces. They helped take Hector's bier inside the house, and the minstrels came and sat next to it. Andromache fell on Hector's body crying hysterically. "You are going away young, my husband", she said, "leaving the wives and children of the city and me and your son, unprotected from becoming slaves". Hecuba said, Hector was closest to her heart than any of the other children and he must have been liked by the gods, for his body to be preserved in such a good condition, despite the mistreatment by Achilleus. Helen said, " Hector was dearest to me than any other brother-in-law; I never heard a bitter word from his mouth."

King Priam addressed the men of the city and told them to go to mount Ida to bring wood for the pyre and not be afraid of an attack, as Achilleus had promised a twelve day truce. The Trojans brought wood for nine days; on the tenth day, they placed Hector's bier on top of the huge wood pile and started the fire, which had been burning all day. The eleventh day they quenched the cinders with wine, before his brothers and friends gathered Hector's white bones; they wrapped them in fine purple cloth and placed them into a golden urn. The urn was then placed in a grave, with a monument of large stones built over it.

XII. HELP TO TROY BY THE AMAZONS AND THE ETHIOPEANS ENDS IN DISAPPOINTMENT.

Hector's death was a big blow to the moral of the city. Desperation covered the citizen's faces. The only protection they could see, although temporary, were the walls of the city. But Priam felt responsible to do whatever he could to save the city and sent emissaries to all the friendly people he knew to ask for help. A few days later the Amazons arrived. The Head of the Amazon army was Pentheselea, well known for her extreme bravery and beauty. She sounded confident that she could defeat any man, including Achilleus. The Trojans felt embarrassed for their pessimism. The next day they gladly joined the Amazon army for an attack. The Achaians were caught by surprise and suffered severe losses, close to their camp. Achilleus and Ajax were talking, when they saw the battle approaching. They immediately armed themselves; but before they had a chance to move they had to confront this imposing figure on a marvelous horse; it was Pentheselea. Without hesitation she hurled a spear at each one of them, which they both stopped with their shields. Ajax went after the Trojans, leaving Achilleus to deal with the rider. Achilleus also threw two spears against her, the first wounding her slightly; the second mortally, with her and her horse spread over the ground. Achilleus pulled her helmet from her head and was amazed to see a woman with such beauty. "I don't know why this woman wanted me dead, when she could have me totally hers, alive, as my queen." Achilleus exclaimed.

With the loss of Pentheselea the Trojans again ran to the safety of their walls, and for them things returned to desperation. In a council meeting there were proposals of abandoning the city, but Priam rejected such ideas. In fact as they were talking guards ran into the meeting announcing that a whole army was spotted in the plain advancing on the city. Judging from the black horses, Priam concluded it was his friend Memnon, son of the goddess Io, king of the Ethiopians, with his army. This was excellent news and preparations were immediately made for Memnon's reception, which turned into a feast that lasted till late that evening.

In the morning, Trojans and Ethiopians mounted a coordinated attack, with the hope to took the Achaians by surprise. But when they reached close to the Greek camp they found the Achaians armed and the Myrmidons with Achilleus in charge, ready to defend their ships. Memnon happened to find Nestor on his way and raised his sword against him, when his son Antilochus got in between the two, with his own sword. After a few seconds, Antilochus fell down dead, his chest pierced by Memnon's sword. Nestor called Achilleus to protect his son's body and when Memnon saw him he bragged Achilleus was now going to pay for what he had done to the Trojans; for his mother Io, lived up on Olympus, while Thetis, a lesser god, was living at the bottom of the sea. "Let us wait and see", Achilleus responded with a smile. The time was passing with each able to defend against the other's attacks with his shield, and sometimes with his helmet. The battle around them stopped and everybody was watching the two experienced fighters. The gods too, from the top of Olympus, all turned their attention to this single combat. Finally Zeus called for the Fates of the combatants; a dark one appeared for Memnon, a bright for Achilleus. The Fates came down and stood next to the fighting men, unseen by them. Immediately, Achilleus pierced Memnon's chest. Io jumped from her seat and raised black clouds over the battlefield, while she ordered the winds to support Memnon's body and carry it away, as his soldiers were watching. Panic soon spread in the Trojan and Ethiopian ranks, and they all ran to the walls of Troy for shelter.

XIII. ACHILLEUS' END.

The Achaians could not rejoice for their victory with Antilochus dead. He was Achilleus' best friend next to Patroclus, and his loss intensified his wounds. Again he sought revenge, and he ran after the Trojans killing as many as he could, till he reached the Skaian gate, which was closed before he got there. He pounded on it with his fists and shook it, trying to tear it down. At this point Apollo got concerned and flew down from Olympus. "Hold back your fury son of Pellius, or you will have to answer to the gods," he said. Achilleus recognized the voice and answered, "Don't bother me Phoebus, you are always against me, you better go back where you came from for you may be a god, but I am holding a long spear." Apollo ran into a dark cloud, and directed an arrow straight at Achilleus heel, the only vulnerable part of his body. A sharp pain went through his heart, and he looked in vain around to find the coward who sneaked and wounded him. He pulled the arrow out of his heel and threw it away, while he kept fighting all around him. Apollo picked his arrow and left; with the loss of blood, Achilleus' vision darkened, his knees became stiff, and he fell among the Trojans, who could not believe their eyes. At first, none dared come near his body. But when Paris saw Achilleus down, he claimed he had killed Achilleus and urged the Trojans to capture and bring the body into the city, where they could give it the treatment Hector received from Achilleus. Ajax ran and stood over the body of Achilleus fighting anyone who dared approach. Odysseus then arrived, and despite his wound, he was able to help take the body away and bring it to Achilleus' tent. Ajax and Agamemnon kept looking at the ground to hide their tears, while Briseis, as beautiful as ever, was hysterical, lamenting over Achilleus' body. "My sweet", she said, "you are going away, and I feel my life is also over, for you were my family, my consolation for my misfortunes, you were a holy day for me even though I was your slave. When Thetis with her sisters heard Briseis, they knew what they were already lamenting, had happened, Achilleus was dead. They left the cave and tore through the waters of the sea of Hellespont, where they could be seen moving with the waves. Thetis, followed by a few of her sisters, went directly to Achilleus tent, where she embraced her son, kissing him, while her tears were raining over his body. They stayed lamenting all night, while the Achaians stayed outside, with respect.

In the morning Thetis and her sister Nereids left; then, for seven days, the army came to pay their respect and cry for Achilleus, and also for themselves. The Achaians got busy to fetch wood and prepare for the pyre. They figured what they should do for Achilleus would be what he himself had organized for Patroclus. The entire army stood fully armed around the wood pile. They placed Achilleus at the top and lit the wood, which quickly flared and swallowed Achilleus bier. They stood there all night as the sparks, the flames and the smoke reached the sky. The sky responded with a rain of mournful gray ashes. When the fire subsided, the Myrmidons, quenched the remaining flames and cinder with wine; then they gathered Achilleus bones and placed them in the same urn with those of Patroclus. His horses broke their reins and tried to run away, for they did not want to continue being among mortals.

As was the custom, the funeral followed competitive games, and this time Thetis herself came, first to announce, and then to distribute the prizes to the winners. At the end, she stood up again and said, "I have one more thing, my son's armor, the one Hephaestus made especially for him, and please let the brave man who saved my son's body from the Trojans come forth to receive it. Two men, Ajax and Odysseus, stepped forward to claim the uniform. None of the leaders accepted to offer an opinion, for either of the contestants. Finally, Nestor suggested to have prisoners decide. They brought the prisoners who heard the account of the witnesses and decided that Odysseus deserved to receive the uniform for it was his wisdom that helped pull the body away at the right time. Odysseus was delighted; but Ajax was heartbroken with the decision ready to collapse, had his friends not supported him. That night, he became paranoid and ran around killing whatever sheep he found. Later, he went back to his tent and committed suicide. The Achaians had one more of their best to lament for, and bury. Most of all, Odysseus was remorseful for the death of his friend, to which somehow he had contributed.

The Achaians now found themselves at a disadvantage, after losing two of their bravest, Achilleus and Ajax. Menelaos called for a general assembly, as the morale of the troops was at its lowest. Sear Calchas encouraged the gathering by reminding them of the oracle that they would occupy Troy after ninth years of fighting, and pointed out that the time had come. He stated that they should bring in Neoptolemos, Achilleus son, to replace him and the champion archer Philoktetes, commander of the Thessalians, whom the Achaians had abandoned in Lemnos on the way to Troy because of a foot infection, to replace Ajax. Diomed with Odysseus arranged for a twenty man rowboat with which they went, found and fetched the two to the Achaian camp. However, upon arrival of the boat, the Achaians were in a new crisis. Eurypylos, one of the Trojan allies had arrived at Troy with his army the previous day and together with the Trojan army mounted an attack that had driven the Achaians all the way back to their wall. Odysseus gave Neoptolemos his father's uniform in which he looked very much like his father. He took twenty Myrmidons and stood at the top of the wall. The Trojans thought they were looking at Achilleus' ghost and ran away, with Neoptolemos chasing them. But, Eurypylos' army was not retreating, and was marching ahead with him leading the attack. The two leaders found themselves face to face. Neoptolemos threw his father's famous long spear and instantaneously killed Eurypylos, setting his army into panic. With the crisis over, Agamemnon invited Philoktetes to his tent for dinner and apologized for leaving him behind ten years earlier. He immediately called his best doctor to attend to Philoktetes' wound.

The Trojan moral now had fallen and again Polydamas suggested they stay and protect themselves inside the walls. Aeneas, now in Hector's position objected, and organized a counter-attack. Paris, next to Aeneas, kept encouraging him to annihilate the Achaians. When Paris saw Philoktetes doing so much damage with his arrows, he saw the opportunity for glory, he aimed and sent one of his poisonous arrows against him. Philoktetes avoided Paris arrow and let one of his poisonous arrows fly at Paris chest. The pain immediately spread all over his body. He asked his men to quickly bring him to his former wife, Oinone, who now lived on mount Ida, for she had the power to heal. Paris fell on his knees begging her for help; but she was very bitter about him abandoning her for the sake of Helen and refused. Paris lasted only a few steps away from her house, and fell on the ground dead. His men together with the shepherds, who used to be his old friends, gathered wood and burned his body. While the flames were at their highest Oinone remembered the love she once had for Paris. She came and threw herself next to his body, where they were both transformed into smoke and ashes.

XIV. THE TROJAN HORSE.

At this time most of the legendary fighters from both sides were gone. On the Achaian side Agamemnon, Menelaos, Diomed, Odysseus, and Neoptolemos were still around; while on the Trojan side only Aeneas. The Achaians expected Troy to fall according to Calchas' oracle so they surrounded Troy, trying to climb over the walls, with great losses. Often, the city under attack was covered with fog, which the Achaians interpreted an act of the gods to save the city and retreated in terror. Sear Calchas, saw things were not working as expected, and thought, maybe they were trying too hard with brute force. During a council meeting, he suggested, perhaps they should use their heads, instead of just their muscles. He told them he saw a sign, probably from the gods. He saw a falcon chasing a pigeon, which ran into a crack in the rock, where the falcon could not get in, so as long as the falcon stood by the edge looking in, the pigeon didn't budge. There was obviously a standstill, until the falcon used its head, and pretended to fly away; but returned and hid itself behind the rock. The pigeon, thinking the falcon was gone, came out to fly away, but didn't go far before the falcon was on top of it. The sign certainly impressed the leaders, especially Odysseus, who immediately came up with a plan; he suggested they use wood to build a horse, big enough for many brave men to hide in its belly, and offer it to the temple of the goddess Athena in Ilion. That they should burn their camp, get into their boats to pretend they had abandoned their aspiration to capture Troy, and decided to return home. They should leave one person behind to convince the Trojans to move the horse into the city. The fleet would actually go and hide behind Tenedos island, and come back during the night. The army would then position itself outside Troy, until a signal from a lighted torch from high on the wall could be seen given by one of their men from the horse's belly in Troy, while the other hidden men would open the gates for the Achaian army to enter the city. The plan sounded great to everyone, except Philoktetes and Neoptolemos who thought they had the strength to capture Troy with the glory of bravery, rather than with fraud and deceit. Lightning and thunder from Zeus that instant, convinced every one the objection was not to the liking of the gods, and general agreement prevailed.

The Achaians went right to work. First they went on Mount Ida to find and bring the right wood for the construction of the horse. Epeios, the best carpenter and wood artist was put in charge. He chose the trees to cut, and the men to assist in the construction, which would have taken a long time if it wasn't for goddess Athena, who helped finish it in just three days. The time then came for the brave volunteers to hide inside the horse. Odysseus pointed out that it would take guts to hide in a dark space for so many hours and the consequences in case they were discovered, were actually more than going to battle, but he was ready to go. Neoptolemos,

Beautiful virgins danced and threw flowers on the horse.

Philoktetes, Diomed, Menelaos, and fifteen others, Including Epeios, volunteered. When everything was ready and night came, they burned what ever they had built in their camp, including the wooden portion of their protective wall. While still dark the volunteers entered the horse and closed the trap door. In the morning, the Achaians pulled their boats into the water and loaded with their belongings; then they boarded their ships, raised the sails and left.

The Trojans kept looking all night at what was going on from the top of their wall, it looked like the enemy was giving up, but they couldn't really believe it until they saw the ships sail away. They ran to the seashore to make sure, and there they saw this huge strange-looking horse, with a Greek soldier, named Sinon, grieving nearby. When they asked him, he said the Achaians were going back to their homes, and left the horse behind for the sake of Athena, according to an oracle to gain favorable winds. That they had randomly chosen him for sacrifice but that he ran and asked Zeus's protection underneath the holy horse, from where they did not dare get him.

Simon added that they made a large horse so it could not be moved to the city, but stand on the seashore as a guard until they ask the oracle at Delphi whether they should come back someday. There was a lot of disagreement among the Trojans, some said they should bring it to the city to please Athena, others suggested they should leave it there, and still others thought they should destroy it. One of them, Laocoon, actually guessed the entire Achaian's trickery and threw his spear at the horse. A lot of Trojans paid attention to what he said, but Athena intervened, and had two huge snakes come up from the water, hissing loudly and with flames shooting out of their eyes.

The Trojans panicked and ran to hide in Athena's Temple in the city. The sign was immediately interpreted that Laocoon's remarks were offensive to Goddess Athena, who wanted the horse in her temple. They came back with ropes and wheels to move the horse to the city; there they had to tear part of the wall down to get the horse through, while beautiful virgins were dancing about and throwing flowers on the horse. Cassandra was the only one that protested, for she had prophesied flames coming out of the horse's belly and burning the city. She grasped a flaming torch and tried to burn the horse, but the Trojans took the torch away from her and locked her in the palace. Everyone then joined the celebration with a lot of food and plenty of wine. Soon they were all drunk, asleep. Quiet and stillness spread all over the city. Even the dogs stopped barking. Helen, who had heard Cassandra's warnings, could not sleep, for she was suspecting fowl play by the Achaians. She walked to the temple under the horse and started calling the names of the leaders she suspected might be hiding inside the horse. Menelaos was greatly moved when he heard Helen's voice, and Odysseus covered his mouth lest he responded to her calling.

XV. THE SACKING OF TROY.

When Helen left, the door on the side of the horse's belly opened, and Diomed jumped out to scout around and see if it was safe for the others to exit. He went to the highest point of the wall with a lighted torch to give the signal to the Achaians waiting outside. Then he reported back to the others, still waiting inside the horse, that everything was safe. They all came down from the horse and each ran to the post pre-assigned him. They killed the guards, whom they found asleep, and opened the doors for the Achaian army to enter. The Trojans had no chance to defend themselves. Most of the men were killed while still drunk. They were screams all over the city as the women and children were captured and lead to the ships. The Achaians were taking away whatever they thought valuable, then they torched the houses.

The goddess of Troy was frantic, but could do nothing but cry for her bitter destiny. Neoptolemos entered the palace and found Priam alone. As soon as Priam saw him he recognized him, "I wished your father had killed me when I met him, so I wouldn't live to see the destruction of whatever I have loved. Now, I beg you, do me the favor and get me out of my misery", he said, and Neoptolemos felt he had to

88

grant the old man's wishes and obliged him with a single hit of his sword. We are not quite sure of what exactly happened to Hector's son, Astyanax. Some say an Achaeans soldier threw the boy down from the top of the wall; but according to other accounts, Andromache took the boy with her to Greece, where she was brought as a slave. There, she always felt the boys' life was in danger and asked the help of prominent individuals such as Orestes, Agamemnon's son, for help in saving him. While Troy was being destroyed, Menelaos was running all over the city looking for Helen. Finally, he found her hiding in the basement of the palace. He was furious and drew

The goddess of Troy could do nothing but cry for her bitter destiny.

his sword to kill her, but Aphrodite added even more beauty to her face and body so Menelaos was disarmed. He reasoned there were many questions she should live to answer. So they joined the endless line of women and children walking toward the ships, to slavery. Among them was Cassandra who was captured by Agamemnon to become his slave, and Andromache, whom Neoptolemos said he wanted. Hecuba was given to Odysseus. Helen walked to the ships without uttering a word. She just looked at the ground to avoid the eyes of people around. Nobody dared to say a caustic word about her. They were looking at her beauty and understood why they were there. That night Helen and Menelaos found themselves in the boat alone. She fell on her knees and asked for forgiveness. She said she did not know to what extent Aphrodite had fogged her mind, but she was ready to assume full responsibility for her action. Menelaos picked her up and told her not to be afraid and that he could never stop loving her. The couple were back together. Few Trojan men survived the onslaught of Troy, only those who were able to escape to Mount Ida. Aeneas, was one of them; he picked up his old father on his shoulders, while holding the hand of his young son Askanios. After living on Mount Ida for awhile, he traveled west, to Italy, where some claim he was one of the founders of Rome.

Next day the Achaians, loaded their ships with supplies, treasures and slaves. Calchas announced that the gods required the sacrifice of a princess, before they were ready to provide good weather for their return. They found, among the prison-

With favorable wind each ship raised its sale and left the coast of Troy

ers, Polyxene, Priam's daughter. Hecuba, had to witness one more disaster, the sacrifice of her beautiful Polyxene. The East wind came, the ships were ready and the leaders went up on the front deck of the ships, with cups full of red wine, which they poured onto the waves as they prayed to the gods for a good journey home.

90

Xanthus, Achilleus' immortal talking horse, still mourns